GREAT EVENTS
IN THE LIFE OF
LEIF ERICSON

5 *Hears from Bjarni about lands discovered to the west, 988*

6 *Sails from Greenland to Norway in history's first transatlantic voyage, 999*

8 *Discovers and explores Vinland, 1002*

7 *Becomes a Christian and returns to Greenland, 1000*

THE STORY OF
Leif Ericson

"Leif Ericson gives way to no man,"
he replied

THE STORY OF
Leif Ericson

By WILLIAM O. STEELE

Illustrated by PRANAS LAPÉ

ENID LAMONTE MEADOWCROFT
Supervising Editor

PUBLISHERS Grosset & Dunlap NEW YORK

To the Two Loulies
GRANDMOTHER JOHNSTON
GRANDMOTHER STEELE

PRINTED IN THE UNITED STATES OF AMERICA

Library of Congress Catalog Card No. 54–5862

Contents

[*v*]

Illustrations

ILLUSTRATIONS

THE STORY OF
Leif Ericson

The sun never melted the snow there

CHAPTER ONE

On Ox Island

Hurry up, Tyrker!" shouted Leif Ericson.

He stood on a stone wall, balancing himself with outstretched arms. The wall ran all around the farm buildings which belonged to his father, redheaded Eric. The farm was on an island, and a warm April breeze blew from the sea.

"Hurry up," Leif shouted again.

"I'll be there soon enough," Tyrker the German answered from inside the smithy. He had been mending a sword hilt. Now he hung the great bellows back on the wall and began to sharpen a knife.

Leif heard the whir of the grindstone and sighed impatiently. He looked out across the farmyard and saw one of the servants going

[*3*]

toward the dairy. The dairy was a big stone building. But it was not as big as the three barns for his father's horses and his many cattle.

"The buildings inside the stone wall make a little town," Leif thought.

And the big farm *did* seem like a little town. Besides the barns and the dairy there were a good many small houses where Eric's servants and slaves lived. And there were also the smithy, a temple, and a springhouse.

But larger than any of these was the huge feast hall. It was a long wooden building with a high, steep roof. Smaller rooms had been added at one side of the hall. These windowless rooms were sleeping and dressing rooms for Eric's family and friends. They, too, had sharply sloping roofs, but not so high as the roof of the feast hall.

Eric was a prosperous man, well thought of in Iceland. Some day all of his farm on Ox Island would belong to Leif, for he was the eldest son. But eight-year-old Leif was not much interested in farming.

"I'd rather go sailing to faraway lands," he told himself as he took a few steps along the wall. "When I'm grown up I don't want to stay on Ox Island, or on the mainland either."

He turned and looked across the water toward the mainland. He could see the rocky shore sloping up toward grassy meadows. In the distance was a range of mountains. Their tops were white with snow. The sun never melted the snow there. It was so bright that Leif squinted his eyes. Then he heard Tyrker call him.

"Come along. I'm ready," Tyrker said from the door of the smithy.

Leif jumped from the wall. He walked beside Tyrker until they came to the steep path which led down to the beach on the south side of the island. They were going to look for driftwood. When they reached the top of the path, Leif began to run.

"Not so fast, Leif," called Tyrker.

But the boy paid no attention. Swiftly he sped down the zigzagging path that led to the sand below. Near the bottom of the path, Leif sprang to the top of a boulder.

"Don't jump!" warned Tyrker.

Leif leaped with arms outstretched to the sand twelve feet below him.

Tyrker gave a cry and ran around the boulder. Leif stood with folded arms. "Are you hurt?" the German asked anxiously.

"Of course not," Leif answered scornfully. He looked out across the fiord. The fiord was a narrow arm of the Atlantic Ocean which cut into the coast of Iceland. Ox Island was one of many islands at the mouth of the fiord.

"It's only the goodness of the god, Thor, that saved you, then," grumbled the man. "You'll break your neck some day. You're just like your father—rushing into things without waiting to count the dangers. He's always in trouble. I hope you learn to look before you leap, long before you're his age."

"There are the fishing boats yonder," exclaimed Leif, pointing.

The two stood gazing across the water of the fiord. They made a strange contrast. Tyrker the German was a man about forty years old. His dark eyes shone in his ugly face with its turned-up nose. He was short and stocky, and his legs were bent and bowed so that he was not much taller than Leif.

The boy was tall for his eight years, straight and well built. His eyes were blue. His fair hair came down to his shoulders.

"Your eyes are sharp," said Tyrker at last. "I see no boats."

Tyrker the German was short and stocky

"I wish I could see farther than the boats," Leif replied. "I wish I could see on and on, over the horizon of the ocean. What do you suppose lies out there, Tyrker?"

"Who knows?" the German answered. "The edge of the world. Strange lands full of strange people with perhaps only one leg or three heads. That's not the direction I'd look, if I had eyes that could see beyond the sea's rim."

He turned and looked toward the southeast, where Germany lay. Many years before, he had been captured by Viking raiders and taken from his home there. He had been sold as a thrall, or slave, to Eric the Red. But Eric had grown fond of his good-natured, homely thrall and had given Tyrker his freedom.

The German was an intelligent man, skilled in many crafts. When Eric's son, Leif, was born, Eric had made Tyrker the child's foster father. It was Tyrker's duty to watch over Leif and to teach him whatever he must know.

"Would you like to see your old home again?" asked Leif.

"Sometimes I long to see the great forests of Germany," admitted Tyrker. "There are so few trees here in Iceland. But I've been away so long, I doubt if I'd recognize my home."

"My father doesn't seem to miss his old home in Norway," said Leif. "Did you come to Iceland with him when he was banished from Norway, Tyrker?"

The German nodded. "Yes, I came with Eric to Iceland," he said. "I remember that time well. Your father was banished from Norway because he had killed a man in a duel. Thirty thralls rowed us across the water and we settled in the northwestern part of Iceland. But later your father got into a second fight and was banished again. So we came here to Ox Island. That second fight wasn't really all his fault, though."

"How did it happen?" asked Leif, who liked to hear stories about his father.

"Two of Eric's thralls accidentally caused a landslide," Tyrker went on. "It ruined a neighbor's house and killed the neighbor. A kinsman of the neighbor killed the thralls, which was not right, and Eric got angry and killed the kinsman."

The German shook his finger at Leif and added sharply, "You'll learn someday that it pays to think twice before you act."

[9]

Hastily Leif picked up a stone and threw it at a puffin flying along the water's edge.

"I hit him!" he cried. "Did you see that throw, Tyrker?"

"You have a keen eye and a strong arm, Leif," Tyrker answered. "It would be a strange thing if you couldn't hit a bird that flies as slowly as a puffin. Now let us look for a piece of driftwood the right size for a rudder handle."

They began to walk down the beach. There were few trees in Iceland and every piece of driftwood was treasured. Leif often spent hours searching the rocky shores for driftwood.

"When I find a piece that's large enough," Tyrker told Leif, "I'll carve it in a special way. I dreamed the other night that the god Thor himself spoke to me and told me certain symbols to carve on a rudder handle for your father's boat. He said the symbols would protect your father from stress and trouble. And your father needs protection if anyone ever did."

"Look! Here come my cousins!" cried Leif suddenly.

Two young men came down a steep path which led to the beach. Leif's cousins were

about fifteen years old. Soon they would be
real warriors and chieftains in Iceland. They
were visiting Eric from their homes on the
mainland. Leif admired them very much. In
the three months they had been on the island,
he had tried often to get them to pay him some
attention. But they never did. They thought
Leif was a baby, too young for their notice.

"Where are you going?" cried Leif.

"We're going to swim out to the rocks
yonder," answered Bolli.

"Let me come," begged Leif.

"You! You baby. What would you do out
there with men?" scoffed Grim.

"I'm not a baby," Leif answered indig-
nantly. He pulled up the sleeve of his brown
shirt and pointed to a long scratch on his arm.
"Yesterday, Tyrker and I fought with real
swords, not wooden practice ones. And see, I
have a battle wound!"

"A battle wound!" cried Grim. "That
scratch! Wait till you have something like
this." He opened his shirt and showed a great
ugly red scar across his chest and shoulder. He
said proudly, "I got that this winter. I went
with some others to seek out Gunnar the Hog
who murdered the captain of his fishing boat."

[*11*]

"Stay here, baby Leif, and play with your toys," grinned Bolli.

Leif started to answer, but the older boys turned away from him. They began to strip off their clothes and weapons. In a few minutes the two plunged into the cold fiord. With strong strokes they swam toward a pile of rocks several hundred feet from shore.

Leif watched his cousins a moment in silence. He did not like to be called a baby. He muttered to himself, "I'll show them who's a baby."

He glanced along the beach. Tyrker was still looking for the driftwood he needed. He had his back to Leif.

Quickly Leif stripped off his woolen shirt and breeches. Flinging them to the sand, he splashed out into the fiord. A wall of water rushed toward him. He dived through the wave and came up swimming evenly.

It was windy and the fiord was rough. But Leif had learned to swim in rough water. The fiord around Ox Island was seldom calm. He kicked his feet harder.

A wave carried him up so that he saw his cousins climb out on the rocks.

Leif swam steadily on. Soon he began to tire.

The waves were rougher farther out from shore. He shook water from his eyes and glanced ahead. The rocks seemed a long way off. In spite of all his swimming, he had not come very far. He thought of turning back.

"But I'm no baby. I'll go on," Leif told himself.

His arms were tired. They were beginning to feel as heavy and hard to lift as his father's great battle sword. He could hardly move his legs either.

It was certainly much farther to the rocks than he had thought. No, the trouble was, he hadn't thought at all. Tyrker was right. He rushed into things without thinking them out first.

A wave broke around him suddenly. His mouth filled with salt water. He coughed and spluttered. He fought to hold his head out of the water. He felt sure he was going to drown.

"But I won't give up yet," he told himself. "I'll keep on trying. I'll call on Thor for help."

He coughed again.

"Help me, Thor!" he cried silently.

Wearily he pushed one arm forward, then the other, and gave a feeble kick.

Suddenly a hand seized him by the hair.

"Climb on my back!" cried Grim in his ear.

Leif clung to Grim's shoulders and the older boy swam to the rocks a short distance away.

"Little fool!" cried Grim angrily as he dumped Leif on the rocks. "It was only the good luck you got from your father that saved you. If I hadn't come around on this side of the rocks to try a dive, you would have drowned."

"Has the baby drowned himself?" laughed Bolli.

"Nearly," answered Grim. "Only his luck kept him afloat in that sea. He must have been spellbound to try such a swim."

"My father says," gasped Leif, getting his wind back at last, "my father says a man must use all of his strength for doing a deed."

"He must use all of his strength," answered Grim. "But it is tempting the gods if he tries to use more strength than he has. Boys must wait till they are men before they take up men's ways."

He turned and measured the distance to shore with his eyes. "But it was a bold try, cousin," he said with a laugh. "Perhaps you are not the baby we called you, after all."

CHAPTER TWO

Tyrker's Prophecy

"WHERE in the name of Odin are my gold spurs?" bellowed Eric. He was on his knees searching through the carved wooden chest impatiently. He looked around at his son with a scowl. "Leif, fetch Tyrker here."

Leif hurried from the sleeping room. As he walked, he could feel his scarlet cloak float out from his shoulders. He stopped at the entrance to the hall and ran his hand down the tight leg of his blue silk breeches. They were just like Eric's except for the color, and Leif was proud of them. Over his woolen undershirt he wore a shirt his mother had woven of fine white linen and embroidered in red. He was wearing his best clothes, for he was going to a feast.

He stepped into the great hall. Here the

family ate, and here the feasting and good times took place. Today it was dark and empty. The windows in the roof were shuttered. Only the smoke hole let in light. There were no chimneys to let out the smoke of the fires, which were built on stone hearths down the center of the hall. The smoke escaped through the big hole in the roof.

Now there was only one fire at the far end of the hall. Tyrker sat on a stool staring into the flames. He looked half asleep.

"I won't call him," Leif told himself. "I'll creep up quietly and jump at him. I'll make old Tyrker yell!"

He grinned as he tiptoed over the stone floor. The walls on each side of the hall were hung with shields, swords, and battle axes. There were many tapestries picturing famous battles and stories of Viking heroes. Leif liked to look at these, but he liked better the stories which were carved on the dais boards.

A platform, or dais, ran along one wall of the hall. On the dais were the benches where Eric and his most important guests sat during feasts. Boards usually paneled the front of this dais. They were richly carved with tales of the gods, Thor and Odin and the rest. But one

Tyrker sat staring into the flames

day Eric had lent the boards to a neighbor who admired them. Leif paused and looked at the black hole where the dais boards belonged. He wished his father would get them back.

There was a muffled roar from Eric's sleeping room. Leif remembered his errand and hurried down the long hall. As he reached the fireplace, the German turned his head toward the boy.

"I have Eric's gold spurs," he murmured. "I polished them. Tell him I'll bring them."

Leif stood still in surprise. How had Tyrker known that Eric wanted his spurs? How had he known Eric had sent him to ask about them? Indeed, how had he known that Leif was in the hall? The boy had been as quiet as a stalking hawk.

For a moment Leif felt very strange. Was it true that Tyrker had second sight and knew what was going to happen before it happened? Leif's mother said he did. What had the German seen as he gazed into the fire?

A piece of burning peat fell on the hearthstone. Tyrker stood up and kicked it back into the fire.

Leif stared at his familiar squat figure.

Later perhaps he would ask Tyrker if he could tell what was going to happen at the feast. He hoped there would be a horse fight. If Tyrker really could see into the future, he ought to be able to foresee a horse fight.

Quickly Leif ran back to his father's sleeping room. "Tyrker has the spurs," he said. "He took them so he could polish them, Father."

Eric turned and his red cloak swirled behind him. It was embroidered in blue and yellow thread. So were his tight green breeches. His shirt was of the finest white linen.

Leif looked with envy at the armor of chain mail which Eric wore over his linen shirt. Even though he was going to a feast, Eric went prepared for a fight. Viking chieftains and their followers were proud and hot-tempered. Almost anything might start a fight among them. There were laws in Iceland, but not very much authority to enforce them. There was always danger from robbers. And there were also men who held grudges against Eric and who might attack him on the way to the feast.

However, Eric had strips of white cloth, called peace bonds, tied across his jewel-encrusted scabbard. These were a sign that

[*19*]

he went to the feast on friendly terms with everyone.

"Tyrker might have told me about my spurs," he growled. "I thought I would have to go to the feast with common bronze spurs jingling at my heels."

Tyrker came in with the spurs gleaming in his hand. He knelt to fasten them to Eric's heels.

Leif's mother, Thorhild, entered, wearing a long white kirtle or gown, caught at the waist by a jeweled belt. There was a gold band around her head. She smiled at Leif and said, "How fine you look, Leif! I am glad your new shirt was finished in time for the feast."

Thorstein dashed by his mother and into the room. He was five and was going to his first feast. The youngest brother, Thorvald, would stay at home with his nurse, for he was only two.

Thorstein was feeling very grown up and important. "Look, Leif!" he cried, holding up his hands. From each of his wrists hung a gold bracelet, like those which Eric and Leif and Thorhild wore. "I wish I could wear a sword," Thorstein added sadly.

Leif smiled at his brother. Though he himself was not yet old enough to wear a sword, he carried a very beautiful knife at his belt. He touched it lovingly. He knew how Thorstein felt.

A short, dull-edged dagger lay on a chest near by. Suddenly Leif caught it up and thrust it into Thorstein's belt. "There!" he exclaimed. "Now you have a weapon. If robbers attack us, you can kill them all!"

A horse neighed outside and another answered. There were the sounds of pawing hoofs and Leif heard Tyrker shout, "Keep that horse away from Eric's bay, or there'll be a fight!"

"The horses are ready!" cried Leif, running from the room.

"Tell Tyrker we're almost ready too," Eric called after him.

"All right, Father," answered Leif from the anteroom. A moment later he stepped into the farmyard.

Thralls were trying to quiet a number of horses while a stocky little red-faced man pulled on the bridle of a big bay. The animal reared and snorted.

"Hurry up, Becan," commanded Tyrker angrily. "Get Eric's horse away."

Leif watched Becan lead the rearing bay across the yard and heard Tyrker mutter, "That Irish thrall always forgets, no matter how often I tell him."

"Father says he's almost ready to leave," Leif announced. "What's Becan done now?"

"He's just too stupid to handle horses," Tyrker said with a frown. "I wish your father had never bought him."

"Oh, I like Becan," cried Leif. "He can tell wonderful tales of his home and the days before a Viking ship came to his village. He says he and two other men and three women were captured by Vikings and sold here in Iceland."

"Yes, I know," Tyrker broke in. "He's told

me that too. But that doesn't make him able to handle horses. Now let's see, how many horses will we need? Who's going?"

"There are Mother and Father and me and Thorstein," Leif counted. "And there are my aunt Helga and my uncle Hodur and my three cousins."

Tyrker nodded. "They've been visiting for three weeks. Do you suppose they'll ever leave?"

Leif burst out laughing. "Eric likes company, Tyrker. He's even had Thorgils Snorrison visiting here for a week to talk about buying some cattle. And Thorgils only lives three miles away on the mainland."

"Yes, Thorgils is going too," Tyrker went on. "With five armed thralls, that makes fifteen. Yet I've got sixteen horses ready. Who else is going?"

Leif laughed and said, "It's yourself, Tyrker."

"So it is," grinned the German. He turned and called to Becan, "Tie Eric's horse to that iron ring and fetch me my shield I left in the barn. Hurry now, Becan. Eric's ready to leave."

Becan ran toward the barn. Leif turned toward his foster father. This would be a good time to ask him about the horse fight. Maybe Eric would let his spirited bay fight with another horse. That would be something to see!

"Tyrker," Leif asked boldly, "can you really see into the future? Can you tell me what's going to happen at the feast?"

The German was silent. The horses moved about restlessly. A gull flew over the house calling loudly. "Tell me," urged Leif, "I know you can. I want to know if there'll be a horse fight at the feast."

Tyrker turned and looked at him strangely. Leif felt prickles at the nape of his neck.

"That I do not know," Tyrker answered slowly. "But this I can tell you. At the feast, you will make an enemy—an enemy for life!"

The door behind Leif opened and his mother came out. Tyrker went to help her mount.

Leif stared at the German. He was puzzled by Tyrker's words. He moved off toward his shaggy pony and leaped nimbly into the saddle. What did Tyrker mean?

CHAPTER THREE

The Feast

THE feast was at the home of Egil the Bellower. Egil's son had just returned from a
year's visit to Norway and the feast was given
in honor of his homecoming.

Egil lived a three-hour ride from the coast,
at the foot of the snow-covered mountain
which Leif could see from his island. The road
was rough and rocky, and the ride seemed very
long to Leif.

At last Eric's party reached the top of a small
rise. Egil's farm lay below them. Leif saw that
it was a fine one. There were more barns and
storehouses inside the stone farmyard wall
than there were on Ox Island.

Leif could see many horses around the stables. "Look at the horses," he cried. "How many guests will be here?"

"Five hundred, I should say," Tyrker answered. "Egil is a rich and important man.

"That's Egil standing in front of the feast hall," Tyrker pointed out as they rode closer.

As the party reined to a stop before the entrance to the great hall, Egil strode forward with a cry of greeting. Eric jumped from his horse and seized his host in a bear hug, for they were great friends.

Egil then led Eric and his party toward the place where the foreguests stood ready to receive them. Some of the foreguests were Egil's relatives. Others were important men of the neighborhood who were there to welcome arrivals.

As Leif followed his father, he saw a big bird come strolling around the corner of the feast hall. "What's that, Tyrker?" gasped Leif.

The bird had an extraordinarily long tail trailing on the ground behind it. Suddenly it raised its tail and spead it so that the feathers stood up in a huge fan. Gold and blue and green flashed before Leif's eyes.

"What is it?" Leif asked again.

"It's a peacock," Tyrker explained. "Egil

travels a lot and he always brings back strange things. His house is full of them."

"I wish we had a peacock," remarked Leif, watching the bird.

"I'd rather have a goose," said Tyrker. "Peacocks seldom live through our hard winters. Come along, let's go into the hall."

Another party of guests had arrived. The thralls were running and shouting as they led the newcomers' horses to the stables. One horse was rearing. The bright cloaks of Egil's guests billowed in the fall wind like colored clouds.

A delicious smell of roast meat came from the kitchen. Leif sniffed. He was hungry. He walked into the hall. How exciting it was to be in a new place with nothing to do but eat and play games and have fun for three days!

Leif thought he had never seen such beautiful tapestries as those on the wall of the feast hall. He had never before seen such rich carvings as those that decorated the doors, the chairs, and benches. Many of the carvings were filled in with gold. They shone and sparkled in the light of the leaping fires which were burning down the center of the room.

A woman told each guest where to sit as he

came into the feast hall. Where a guest sat was very important, because it showed his rank and how much his host thought of him. Leif himself sat with a group of boys who were sons of chiefs. But he was pleased to see that Eric was seated in the high seat on the opposite side of the hall from Egil's chair. This was the seat reserved for the most honored guest.

Even Leif's uncle, Hodur, sat close to Egil on the right hand. That was a good place to sit also. Leif wondered what a boy felt like whose father had to sit near the doors of the hall, far from either high seat. Of course, Tyrker was sitting near the doors. But he was just a freedman with no property and he expected nothing else.

The tables in front of Eric and Egil were covered with fine linen cloth, but at Leif's table the carved wooden bowls and spoons were set out on the bare boards. Leif seized the horn full of buttermilk which was in front of him and drank the milk quickly. Now servants were coming toward him, bringing big trenchers of meat and fish. Others carried wooden pitchers of mead, a liquor made from honey.

Leif drew his knife from his belt and hacked off a big piece of goose when the platter came to him. He helped himself to the little hard, round loaves of bread, and the sweet butter.

"See those little broiled birds?" the boy next to Leif asked. "My father says Egil had them brought from Scotland. They are very good."

Leif took two of the birds when the trencher was passed. They were delicious, but there was not much meat on the bones. He preferred the big roast of horse meat, swimming in red gravy, that came next.

"Look," another boy nudged Leif. "Yonder behind Egil is his spear, Death Singer." All the men had placed their shields and spears against the wall behind them when they sat down to eat, so that their weapons would be close at hand if they should suddenly be needed.

Leif gazed with awe at the great carved spear. Egil was a mighty warrior, and men said his spear sang a song before it killed an enemy.

"Huh, I guess Egil's not such a warrior as he thinks he is," another boy spoke up. "He's always bragging about where he's been and what he's done. I notice he always goes somewhere else to do his brave deeds, where nobody can see him. We just have to take his word for it when he comes home."

Leif was shocked. What a way to speak

about one's host! The boy who had spoken was a swaggering bully named Gest Olafson. Leif knew him. He wished he had a weapon with him besides his knife. He'd soon teach Gest how a Viking behaved toward the man in whose house he was a guest.

"Oh, keep still, Gest," said the boy who had told Leif about the birds from Scotland. "You're always bragging about yourself and saying rude things about others."

Leif turned away as a tall, ruddy-faced warrior walked to the center of the hall. The warrior began to tell a story about sea battles he had fought with Turkish sailors in a southern sea. It was a very exciting tale and Leif listened to it intently.

Through the rest of the day the feasting and storytelling went on. Leif ate and ate. He began to feel stuffed and sleepy. Just as he was about to fall asleep in his seat, Tyrker appeared at his side.

"Come," he said. "I'll show you where you're to sleep."

Leif followed his foster father out of the hall. It was good to be out in the sharp night air, away from the heat and smoke of the hall. He was glad he was not one of those who would sleep on pallets on the feast-hall floor.

Against the outside wall of one of Egil's sleeping rooms, a short flight of stairs led up to the loft. Here a great many pallets for the boys had been arranged. Tyrker showed Leif his, and sleepily Leif stripped down to his long woolen undershirt. He lay down and Tyrker threw a robe over him. In another minute the boy was asleep.

Early the following morning Leif awoke to the sound of swordplay. Already the younger men were practicing for the contests to be held that day. Leif hurriedly dressed. He was anxious to take part in the contests himself and hoped he could win at stone-throwing and archery.

All that morning the contests went on. Leif won an archery contest. His prize was a silver ornament, made in the shape of a small hammer, like Thor's magic one. The hammer was on a silver chain and Leif hung it proudly around his neck.

Leif took part in a good many contests. He almost won the foot race. By afternoon he was tired and glad to go to the feast hall to hear a famous scald.

As Leif passed Tyrker on the way to his seat,

the German whispered, "Listen carefully, Leif. This is Bragi the Bold. He has sung at the court of the King of Norway and is famous all over Iceland."

Leif nodded. Scalds were the poets and historians of the Vikings and they were very highly respected. The Vikings thought that poetry was a gift of the gods. Not every person

was able to compose and sing scaldic verse. Since no history was written down, the records of the great deeds of the Viking heroes were only kept through the scalds' recitations.

Bragi was a tall man with white hair. He stood by his harp which was almost as tall as he was. He struck a few chords. He began to chant:

LEIF ERICSON

"I know spears standing
Around Egil's hall,
Four less than five hundred.
But one of them is best.
It is the serpent of battle.
There is terror in its point."

The scald was telling the story of Death
Singer, Egil's spear. How Egil could throw the
spear so hard that it sang above the heads of
the enemy. How it would kill none but great
enemy chiefs. How Egil had used it in great
Viking raids in England, Scotland, and Ireland.

When the song was over, there were shouts
from the guests.

"Well done, Bragi!"

"Noble poetry!" yelled another.

Egil was much pleased with this song. He
presented Bragi with a gold bracelet made in
the shape of a snake. The head of the serpent
was set with sparkling jewels.

Bragi sang again and again. While Leif listened, he ate heartily of the many dishes that
were passed up and down the table. Late in
the evening a juggler appeared to juggle many
colored balls. Leif was anxious to watch him,
but the day had been too much for him.

Sleepily he stumbled to his bed in the loft.

By the third day, Leif was beginning to be bored with the feast. He was tired of songs and stories. He had eaten so much that he wasn't hungry at all. Not even roast goose with a new kind of stuffing interested him.

He wished there would be a horse fight. Nobody seemed to be anxious to stir up the horses. But perhaps, if he went out by the stables and waited, one of the young men would come down and challenge another's horse to a fight.

He left the smoke-filled, noisy feasting hall and wandered outdoors. From the direction of the barn he heard cries and shouts. He hastened forward and found a group of boys in a circle.

"What's happening?" asked Leif. He tried to look over the heads of the crowd.

A boy turned and said, "Hrut Uggason and Gest Olafson are going to wrestle."

Leif squirmed his way to where he could see the two fighters. They were both big strong boys about twelve. Gest was the bigger.

The two boys had stripped off all their clothes but their breeches. For a moment they stood glaring at each other. Then Gest ad-

vanced and quickly grabbed Hrut. He jerked
the smaller boy off his feet and slammed him
to the ground.

Hrut lay there groaning. At last he shook
his head and struggled dizzily to his feet. Gest
rushed him at once and again threw him to the
ground. There was a thud as Hrut's head hit
the earth. He crawled weakly from the circle.

"Who else will wrestle?" called out Gest in-
solently. "Who's not afraid?"

Hot anger flamed in Leif. He hated Gest,
who was always hurting younger boys and
boasting of his strength.

"I'll wrestle you," he cried, jumping into
the center.

Some of the boys shouted to Leif not to do
it.

Leif felt a touch on his arm. He turned to
find Tyrker staring angrily at him.

"Now see what you have done, you little
fool!" he exclaimed. "What made you think
you could win a fight against someone bigger
and stronger than you? You and your father!
You're just alike."

But he drew Leif to one side and began to
help him take off his clothes. In one hand the
German was holding a big bone from which

he had been gnawing meat. He grasped Leif's bare arm. His greasy fingers slid from Leif's wrist.

Tyrker looked at the boy with a sly look. "There's the answer," he said softly. "There is no rule against greasing your body for a fight. And this fight must be wit against strength, Leif. We'll help the wit along a little bit. Wait for me. I'll be right back." He started for the big kitchen.

As soon as Leif stood in nothing but his tight blue breeches, Tyrker returned with a meat skin. He smeared the boy's back, chest, and shoulders well with the greasy skin.

"Now," he chuckled, "let's see the bully hold you." He sobered and looked into Leif's blue eyes. "Mind you, Leif, don't get mad and rush at him, or you'll lose. Wait for an opening."

Leif nodded solemnly and stepped into the circle. He stood facing Gest and felt his heart beat faster. The other boy was even bigger than he'd thought. He would never be able to beat Gest. Why hadn't he kept quiet?

"Leif Ericson, the champion wrestler," Gest sneered. He laughed loudly. "The grease will not help you. It'll be another easy win for me."

[37]

Quickly he charged Leif with arms outstretched to grab him. Leif ducked under Gest's arms and backed away. Gest turned, trying to get a hold on the other's greasy body. His fingers slid off and Leif circled warily away again.

"Stand still, coward!" yelled Gest.

For a moment Leif's eyes blazed with hate. Coward was the worst name anybody could call a Viking. He'd show this bully who was a coward. He charged Gest. As he did so, Gest kicked him hard in the leg.

Leif bit his lip to keep from crying out in pain. His leg throbbed with pain. He limped away from his opponent.

Gest charged after him with a bellowing rush. He wrapped his arms around Leif in a bear hug.

Leif realized this was his chance. He slipped through Gest's arms and jumped quickly behind him. Before Gest could recover, Leif put his knee in the other's back. Grabbing Gest's head, he jerked with all his strength. Gest fell on his back with one arm pinned underneath his body.

The bully moaned and grimaced with pain. He got to his feet with his right arm dangling.

"Stand still, coward!" yelled Gest

"The greasy pig has broken my arm!" he yelled.

The crowd cheered. A boy called out, "No more than you deserved for wrestling boys smaller than you."

Gest glared at the crowd, then he turned to Leif.

"I'll get you for this, Leif Ericson," he called as he stalked off.

The boys hooted at him.

"Hooray for Leif," called one.

"The bully is beaten," screamed another.

Leif was thumped on the back. He felt pleased but shaky. He knew that he would never have won if Tyrker hadn't greased his body.

Turning aside, he saw Tyrker holding his clothes. The little man shook his head.

"You wrestled well, foster son," he said. "But you remember I warned you that you would make an enemy here? Well, you have done it. And a dangerous one, too."

Leif laughed at the German. "Tyrker, you're always worrying," he cried. But in his heart he felt a little strange. Were he and Gest really enemies now? Would they meet again to battle until one or the other should die?

CHAPTER FOUR

Banished!

COME on, Leif, let's go home," begged Thorstein late one summer afternoon.

"Wait. Becan just went aboard the boat with some bags," Leif answered his brother. "When he comes back here to the beach, we'll walk home with him."

The two brothers stood on the sand looking at Eric's dragon ship. The prow with the carved dragon head stood out plainly against the sky which was reddened by the setting sun.

Several thralls were busily engaged in moving boxes and barrels to the hold of the ship. Others were making the ship ready to sail. Redheaded Eric was in trouble once more!

He and his thralls had had a battle with Thorgest, who had borrowed the carved dais boards. In the battle, two of Thorgest's sons

The two brothers stood on the sand

had been killed. Eric was held responsible for the deaths.

Now he was at the Thing, the law court, awaiting his sentence. It might be decided at this court that Eric should be banished from Iceland. If that happened he would have to leave the country immediately. So the thralls were preparing the ship for a quick departure.

Becan came hurrying down the gangplank to the shore. "Ho there!" the Irish thrall called to the boys. "You two are out late. Your mother will be wondering where you are."

"Yes, and I'm hungry," spoke up Thorstein. "Come on, Leif, let's go."

"We'll walk with you, Becan," said Leif. "Is the ship ready to sail?"

Becan shook his head. "No," he answered. "We've loaded the food and water and weapons, as well as the extra sails and oars. But we still have the cattle and horses and their feed to take aboard."

"What was in that last bundle you took on board, Becan?" Thorstein asked.

"Cheese in a skin bag," answered the Irishman, as he reached the top of the steep path. He glanced toward the mainland. "Is that a boat putting off, Leif?" he asked.

[*43*]

"No, there's no sign of a boat," Leif answered. He scanned the shoreline, wishing that he could see his father's boat coming toward Ox Island. What was keeping Eric so long at the Thing?

Thorstein started along the path for home, and Leif and Becan followed behind him.

"Becan, do you think my father will *really* be outlawed from Iceland?" asked Leif.

"Yes, I'm afraid he will be," replied Becan. "Tyrker says Thorgest is a very rich man with lots of friends. Some of the judges at the Thing are friends of his. They'll see that Eric is exiled instead of merely being fined."

"But Thorgest's sons were killed in a fair fight," Leif insisted. "And Thorgest began the fight because he wouldn't give back the dais boards."

"Yes, I know," Becan agreed. "It was a fair fight. The law states that Eric ought only to be fined. But the judges are the ones to say what will happen to him. And I believe they will let Thorgest's gold count for more than the law."

Thorstein dropped back to walk with the others. "Tell us about the fight, Becan," he begged.

"We went to Thorgest's with peace bands on our swords," began Becan. "Thorgest did not want to return the dais boards. But Eric would have them. We took them and left. On the way back to our boat we were attacked without warning. We were outnumbered. Thorgest had his two sons and several thralls with him. But Eric fought like three men. And I did my share."

"What about Tyrker?" asked Leif.

"Oh," answered Becan with a grin, "he did all right for an old man. It didn't take us long to fight our way to our ship."

Leif asked abruptly, "Where will Eric go if he's outlawed, Becan?"

Becan turned to Leif and grinned. "Why shouldn't he go to Ireland and take me with him?"

"I hope he doesn't go back to Norway," Leif mused.

"Well, he could go to the Orkneys or the Shetlands," Becan went on. "I think he has a cousin living in the Orkney Islands."

"Oh, if it were I," Leif exclaimed as they reached a corner of the feasting hall, "I would go sailing to the west and discover a new land."

"You'd better run in and discover your supper," Becan laughed as he walked off toward the barn.

As Leif and Thorstein approached the door of the feast hall, there came a sudden harsh croaking sound overhead.

"Look up yonder," whispered Leif. "There's a raven sitting on the roof."

Thorstein clutched his brother. "Oh, Leif," he cried, "a raven on the house is bad luck."

As the brothers watched, the great black bird drew its head down between its shoulders and croaked three times.

"Oh, Leif, do you think Father is dead?" asked Thorstein in a trembling voice.

"No," Leif answered seriously. "Thor will protect him." His hand crept to the amulet around his neck. It was the hammer he had won at Egil's feast the autumn before.

The raven suddenly took flight and disappeared into the twilight. Leif gripped his brother's arm. "Thorstein, don't tell Mother about this," he commanded. "She's worried enough already. I've seen her going into the temple four times today to sacrifice fowls and pray for Eric's safe return."

"I won't tell," promised Thorstein.

The two boys went inside. Later, as they sat

eating the evening meal, there was the sound of horses' hoofs outside the hall. Thorhild leaped to her feet, knocking a bowl of milk from the table. The great door was flung open and Eric strode into the room.

His face was flushed and angry. At the sight of him Thorhild turned white and sank into her chair.

Eric took his place beside her and roared for meat and drink. A kitchen thrall rushed in with a platter of meat. Another brought bread and a pitcher of mead.

But Eric sat with the food untasted before him, staring into the fire. Tyrker slipped into the hall and took a seat beside the boys. "Outlawed for three years," he whispered to Leif.

"Where will Eric go?" asked Leif.

"Hush," Tyrker answered. "I don't know and Eric is in a rage."

Leif finished his meal and then sat by the fire with his father's greyhound. Suddenly he could stand the waiting no longer. He got up and went to stand by Eric's chair.

Eric continued to stare into the fire and Thorhild motioned Leif away. But Leif put his hand on his father's shoulder. "Father, will you go back to Norway?" he asked.

[47]

"No, you impertinent young whelp," thundered Eric. He turned angrily on the boy, but Leif did not flinch. He looked full into his father's face.

Eric gazed back for a moment and his mood changed. "No, I won't go to Norway," he answered more gently. "Where would you go if you were I?"

Leif smiled. "I would sail west over the ocean's rim," he answered. "I would find a new land and see strange sights."

Eric wrinkled his brow. "By Odin, you would?" He paused and then repeated, "West, you say? West!" He pondered a minute, pulling his red beard. "By Thor's hammer, perhaps the boy's right!" And he pounded his great fist on the table.

Thorhild asked, "Where would you go? There's no land to the west."

"There's the Gunnbjorn Skerries," Eric replied.

"What are the Gunnbjorn Skerries?" asked Leif.

"There was a man years ago named Gunnbjorn, son of Ulf the Crow. He was blown off his course once when he was sailing from Norway to the west coast of Iceland. And far to the west of here he found rocky reefs which were afterwards called the Gunnbjorn Skerries. No one except Gunnbjorn has ever seen them."

"How would you live on rocky reefs?" Thorhild protested in a startled voice.

"There might be land beyond the reefs," Eric replied in a soothing tone. "He who must go a-roving, must take chances."

[*49*]

"Oh, Father, let me go a-roving with you," Leif cried.

"Well, I'll set you a riddle," said Eric. "And if you can answer it, I'll take you with me."

"You will! Tell me the riddle quickly," Leif begged.

Eric recited:

> *"Who are these two*
> *That go to the Thing?*
> *They have three eyes both,*
> *Ten feet,*
> *And one tail have they both.*
> *Thus they pass over lands."*

Leif looked disappointed. He couldn't possibly answer that. "What kind of a creature would have ten legs?" he asked, perplexed. "May I have until tomorrow to answer?"

"Yes," Eric answered good-naturedly. "But you must be up early, for I plan to leave at daybreak."

Thorhild gave Leif a little push. "Now go to bed," she said. "Perhaps the answer will come to you in a dream."

Leif and his brother went to their room. But for a long time Leif lay awake, thinking of the Gunnbjorn Skerries and the ten-legged monster with three eyes.

CHAPTER FIVE

The Flight

LEIF awoke with a start and lay listening. What had he heard?

"Eric, let us in!"

Leif leaped from his bed. Who was pounding at the door? Who had come calling his father in the middle of the night?

"Eric, it's Eyolf. Get up!"

There was the sound of running feet and a dog barking. Leif felt his way through the darkness toward the feast hall. He could hear his father calling for Tyrker. Then there was the sound of the door being unbarred.

It was so dark that Leif kept bumping into walls and doors. By the time he reached the feast hall, the door was barred again. Men were standing around the fire, which Tyrker was building up.

[*51*]

In the light of the leaping flames Leif saw his father, still dressed in his long white nightshirt, and holding his sword in his hand. By him stood his good friends, Eyolf and Styr. Leif knew these two men. They had long been friends of his father and had helped to defend him in the law court.

"Eric, you must leave at once," said Eyolf. "Thorgest will be here before dawn to attack you."

"Then I'll be here to fight him," roared Eric.

"He'll have five ships filled with men," warned Styr. "You couldn't fight so many. You'd best flee."

Eric growled and pulled at his beard. "Eric the Red has never fled from an enemy." He turned toward Tyrker. "Bring mead and drinking horns."

"Don't be foolish, Eric," said Eyolf. "This is no time to fight. You'll be risking not only your own life, but the lives of your family. Sail now and you will have greater honor for it."

Eric strode up and down the great hall, brandishing his sword. Leif could see the queer shadows made by the leaping sword on the tapestries around the hall. He was sure

Leif saw his father holding his sword

that if Eric would only stay, he could defeat Thorgest.

But after a moment Eric turned back to his friends and said, "You're right. I'll sail at once. My ship is ready." He turned and took the pitcher of mead from Tyrker. He filled the horns for himself and his friends.

He raised his horn of mead. "Here's to the downfall of Thorgest. No, wait! I won't drink to that. Here's to my success in finding the Gunnbjorn Skerries!"

Both men stopped with their horns halfway to their lips and stared at Eric.

"The Gunnbjorn Skerries!" exclaimed Styr. "What do you mean?"

"I mean," said Eric calmly, "that I intend to spend my three years of exile looking for the reefs that Gunnbjorn Ulfsson saw to the west of here."

"But no one's seen them since," exclaimed Styr.

"And they're only reefs," Eyolf added. "There's no land there. How will you live?"

"That I will find out," answered Eric. "I would rather live on a rocky reef than live under another chief as I would have to do if I went to a settled land."

"I believe you would, Eric," said Eyolf with a grin. "We'll drink to your success."

All three men raised their horns and drank.

"Tyrker!" shouted Eric. "Wake the thralls! See that the animals are taken on board at once."

Leif shrank back into the shadows. His father was leaving and he was not going to get a chance to go. He had not answered the riddle. What should he do?

Suddenly he thought of a plan. In the excitement nobody would ever miss him. He'd pack his belongings now and go down to the shore. He'd slip aboard the ship and hide among the boxes of food. He'd wait to come out of hiding until it was too late for Eric to turn back.

A short time later he stood outside the house with his hurriedly packed possessions. It was dark, for there was no moon, but the stars shone brightly overhead. There was a great commotion at the barn as thralls dashed about with torches driving out the animals.

Leif ran silently along the path he knew so well. Soon he stood on the beach by the ship. The April night was cool. Leif shivered as he felt his way over the gangplank. He crept forward into the hold and hid. As he settled into a more comfortable position, he could hear the shouts of the thralls, driving the cows down the path. His heart beat wildly with excitement.

The shouts grew louder and louder. The cows mooed in protest. Now he could hear the hoofs on the gangplank while the thralls urged the frightened cattle aboard.

Leif crouched lower. The light from the torches gleamed faintly on his hiding place. There were more shouts and cries and the boat rocked gently under the weight of the cows. Leif thought he could hear his father's voice above the noise.

He heard the oars being put in place. The cows became quieter. Suddenly Thorhild's voice called right over his head, "Thorstein, come back."

"But I can't find Leif anywhere," Thorstein cried.

"What!" exclaimed Eric, "is my eldest son not here to bid me farewell?"

"Perhaps he is with Tyrker," Thorhild suggested.

"No," said Thorstein, "here comes Tyrker."

[56]

"Shall I put this rope in the hold?" Tyrker asked.

"Yes," answered Eric, "and then come help us find Leif."

"Becan, bring your torch over here where I can see," Tyrker commanded the Irish thrall.

Leif trembled and clutched his amulet. "Don't let Tyrker find me," he prayed. He could see Tyrker's legs as he lowered himself into the hold. The German stumbled over a barrel, looking for a safe place to store the rope. Suddenly he gave a startled exclamation.

The next moment Leif felt himself seized by the foot and dragged from his hiding place.

"Let me go, Tyrker," he begged. "Don't tell Eric I'm here."

Tyrker continued to drag him forward.

"Please let me go, Tyrker," cried Leif. "I want to go west and see the Gunnbjorn Skerries."

"What in the name of Thor is going on down there?" shouted Eric, peering into the hold.

"You've got a stowaway, Eric," Tyrker answered, and dragged the boy forth.

"Leif!" exclaimed Thorhild.

Leif struggled to hold back the tears. "Father, let me go," he pleaded. "I don't know the answer to the riddle, but I know I'll be a help to you on the voyage."

Eric burst into a roar of laughter. "What a strange-looking rat you have found in the hold, Tyrker! Cast it overboard."

"Oh, it's not a rat," Thorstein said seriously. "It's just Leif!"

"Well, what's he doing in the hold?" laughed Eric. "Only rats live in the hold."

"Oh, Father, please let me go," Leif begged.

Eric sobered. He placed his hand on the boy's shoulder. "Why, Leif, you are my oldest son. Who would look after your mother and your brothers and the farm if you went with me? Someone must be the man of the house."

Leif looked up at his father. He was only nine years old. He knew he couldn't really be the man of the house. But in three years' time he would be twelve and old enough to take a man's responsibility. He knew what his father meant. His mother would need him. He would have to stay on Ox Island.

"All right, Father," Leif said bravely.

"You're a fine son," said Eric as he put his arm around Leif's shoulder. "Now I must say farewell. Don't worry about me, for my luck goes where I go. I'll return in three years with some fine stories to tell you."

The farewells were made and the family crossed the gangplank to the shore. In the faint

starlight the oars were raised and the boat glided forward. The painted eyes of the dragon gleamed. What would that dragon see, Leif wondered.

Eric shouted an order and for a minute Leif could see the ship in the torchlight as it breasted the waves. Then it was gone.

CHAPTER SIX

Eric's Return

Y OU beat me at wrestling," panted Leif, struggling up from the ground. "But I'll beat you at spear throwing, or throw my arm off trying."

"Well, you won't do it easily," laughed Kettle the Black.

"I'll go get the target," Thorstein said eagerly as he ran off toward the barn.

Tyrker watched the two boys as they put on their shirts. He was glad he had urged Leif to invite Kettle to visit Ox Island. Kettle was a lively lad, a year or so older than Leif. He was nicknamed "The Black" because of his dark coloring.

In the three years since Eric had escaped from Thorgest and sailed in search of the Gunnbjorn Skerries, Leif had changed. He

had grown tall and strong and broad. He had
grown skilled in the use of weapons. His body
was supple and well-trained. Tyrker was
proud of the way he had wrestled Kettle.
Twice Leif had nearly pinned the older,
heavier boy to the ground, and only a des-
perate effort on Kettle's part had given him
the victory.

Leif was nearly a man. He had grown stead-
ier and more serious. Tyrker seldom had to re-
prove him for being impetuous and hot-
headed now. In fact, the old German sometimes thought Leif had grown too serious and
grave for a boy of twelve.

This was the third summer of Eric's banish-
ment. He should have returned some months
before. Tyrker knew that Leif was afraid Eric
was dead. He knew the boy grieved for his father. And he knew that Leif was worried because he might now be responsible for his
mother, his two brothers, all the thralls, and
the great farm.

That was the reason Tyrker was glad to see
Leif enjoying himself with Kettle. "He needs
to be more with boys of his own age," Tyrker
muttered. "Wrestling and spear throwing will
soon take his mind off his troubles."

Thorstein came from the barn, bearing the leather target shaped like a man. He carried it to the end of the meadow.

"Don't stand the target up near the wall, Thorstein," shouted Tyrker. "We don't want the spear points blunted if they should miss the target."

"I won't miss it," Kettle said confidently.

"Actions speak louder than words," Leif answered with a smile. He drew back his arm and sent his spear in a clean arc toward the target. It knocked over the straw-stuffed leather man.

"That was a good throw, Leif," said Kettle. He balanced his iron-pointed spear in his hand, waiting for Thorstein to withdraw Leif's spear from the target. When the target was back in place, Kettle ran a few steps forward and threw.

But he had misjudged the distance. His spear overshot the leather man and struck the soft earth beyond.

"By Thor, your eye is better than mine," admitted Kettle, as Thorstein came toward them with the two spears.

"We'll try again," Leif said. "Perhaps you'll do better next time."

[*62*]

They threw again several times, until Kettle proclaimed that Leif was the better of the two.

"Why don't you move up closer and throw left-handed?" Tyrker asked. "A man is not a spearsman until he can throw as well with one arm as the other."

At the end of a half hour Kettle said, "Maybe I'd better stick to wrestling. No matter which way I throw, I can't beat you, Leif."

"Yes," Tyrker nodded. "When Eric returns, he'll be proud of Leif's skill."

Leif grew sober. "Pray that my father will return," he said. "I have looked for him all summer long. Now I am beginning to think that Eric the Red will never set foot on Ox Island again."

"By thunder, Leif, don't say such things," Tyrker exclaimed. "Eric will come back. His luck will not desert him. Besides, you remember I was the one who carved the rudder of his dragon ship. I carved Thor's name on it and said a special prayer. Such a charm will bring Eric safely home."

"I pray every morning in the temple that it may be so," Leif said. Turning to Kettle, he went on, "Let's go to the cliffs and watch for my father's sail."

"You spend too much time on the cliffs watching," Tyrker grumbled. "Come on to the barn and I'll match Eric's red stallion against the gray I bought last week."

"Oh, let's," exclaimed Thorstein.

"All right," Leif agreed. He was always ready to see a horse fight.

"Is the gray a good horse?" asked Thorstein, as they turned toward the barn.

"He's a fast horse," Tyrker answered. "When he runs, it's as if he had eight legs."

"That would be a sight," chuckled Thorstein. "A horse with eight legs!"

"Odin's horse, Sleipnir, had eight legs," Leif pointed out. He stopped. Was Sleipnir the creature in the riddle Eric had asked him so long ago? He repeated the riddle to himself:

> *"Who are these two*
> *That go to the Thing?*
> *They have three eyes both,*
> *Ten feet,*
> *And one tail have they both.*
> *Thus they pass over lands."*

"No, Sleipnir had only eight legs, not ten," Leif argued with himself. "But wait! If Odin was riding him, Odin had two legs and two and eight make ten." He slapped his thigh. "And Odin had only one eye, so that his one and Sleipnir's two would make the three eyes in the riddle. And of course Sleipnir had a tail. The answer to the riddle is Odin riding his eight-legged horse."

"What is the matter, Leif?" asked Tyrker.

"I've got the answer to that riddle," Leif explained. "If I'd only figured it out three years ago, I could have gone with Father."

"What happened three years ago cannot be changed," Tyrker pointed out. "You boys wait here behind the barn while I get a thrall to help me with the horses."

"I like the gray stallion, I hope he wins," Thorstein remarked as they waited. "I went with Tyrker to buy him."

"I'd rather see the red horse win," Leif said after a moment. "It might be a good omen that Eric the Red would return safely."

"We'll soon see which horse wins," said Kettle. "Here they come."

Tyrker was leading the red horse and a barn thrall led the gray.

"Hold the gray there," commanded Tyrker as he jerked the red horse around. The three boys moved in closer.

"Stand back," Tyrker motioned to them. "I don't want you trampled to death."

The gray lunged forward and jerked his head, trying to pull the halter from the thrall's hand. "Hurry!" cried the thrall. "I can't hold this beast much longer."

The red horse, too, seemed eager for the fray. Tyrker gave a signal and both the bridles were loosened and jerked from the horses' heads. The German scurried to stand with the boys. Several thralls came running to see the fight.

The horses charged, reared in the air and pawed viciously at each other with their forefeet. They came down slashing with their great yellow teeth. The red gashed the gray's neck, and the gray horse shrieked in anger and pain.

The red shouldered the gray horse to one side, trying to bite the other's flank. The gray stepped quickly aside, tearing at the red stallion's neck as he did so. Blood gushed from the wound and splattered in the dust.

Thorstein yelled in excitement, "That gray's going to win!"

Tyrker grunted and moved to get a better view.

Leif leaned forward, watching eagerly.

Once more they reared, neighing ferociously. The red's hoofs struck the gray on the shoulder. The big horse staggered, but recovered quickly. Whirling, he gashed the red across the flank.

At that moment there was the sound of shouting. Leif turned, but Tyrker could not take his eyes from the battling horses. Running across the meadow toward them was one of the thralls, who had been fishing below the cliffs.

"Eric!" gasped the thrall.

Eric! Leif dropped the spear he was still carrying and took to his heels. In two minutes he was stumbling down the path toward the ship landing. When he reached the top of the cliffs, he could see the red and white striped sails of his father's ship below him.

"Father! Father!" he cried, running down the steep path.

Eric, standing on the gangplank, turned at the sound of Leif's voice. In two great strides he had crossed the sandy beach to clasp his son in a bear hug. "By Odin's spear! You've grown,

Leif. Stand off and let me look at you."

Eric thrust Leif back and stared at him. "I almost didn't know you," he said with a shake of the head. "And look at those muscles. Can you wield a battle axe yet?"

"Oh, Father, I was afraid you were dead . . ." Leif began.

"Father!" came a shout from above. Thorstein rushed headlong down the cliff path. And in a few minutes the beach was crowded with thralls and farm workers, overjoyed at their master's safe return.

Later, in the feast hall, Leif thought he would burst with excitement and curiosity. All these greetings and welcomes and hugs and kisses, and still he did not know whether Eric had found the Gunnbjorn Skerries.

He saw Kettle standing a little to one side and knew he ought to go to his guest. But he couldn't do his duty as a host until he knew. He looked around for Becan, whom he had not seen on the beach. The Irish thrall, who had sailed with Eric, would soon tell him the news. But Becan had gone to the kitchen.

Finally, unable to control his impatience any longer, Leif turned to his father. He thrust aside Thorstein, who was standing there.

[*69*]

"Father!" cried Leif. "Did you find the Gunnbjorn Skerries?"

Eric looked down at his tall son. A strange hush fell over all the people in the feast hall.

"Yes," said Eric slowly. "But I found more than the Skerries. I found a whole new land. I found a land so fair that I have called it Greenland. I found a land where no human lives, where no chief can use his gold to do injustice, where no neighbors quarrel with a peaceful man."

"Oh, Father," Leif almost panted with excitement. "Let me sail west. Let me see this new land."

"We'll all see Greenland, Leif," Eric answered. "As soon as I can gather ships and men and stores, I mean to take all of you to this new country. We will settle there within a year, I vow by Odin's spear!"

A gasp went up from the crowd. Leif's mind raced over the sea toward the new land. Just at that moment a thrall appeared with a pitcher of mead. Eric poured some into a horn. Then he stood and lifted the horn high.

"To Greenland!" he shouted. "May it thrive forever!"

CHAPTER SEVEN

Into an Unknown Sea

LEIF stood on the poop deck at the rear of Eric's dragon ship. He took a deep breath. How good the salt air smelled! Leif liked being a sailor, with the wind blowing through his fair hair. He liked the rolling motion of the ship as it plunged through the green waves.

Eric, who sat near by, steering, shouted an order to the rowers. Leif turned and looked back toward Iceland. The mountains were still visible over the edge of the horizon. Scattered over the sea were twenty-five ships. Some were dragon ships like Eric's. Some were heavier, less graceful merchant ships. But all had brightly striped and colored sails.

All the fall and winter after Eric's return from Greenland had been spent in getting this fleet ready. Many of Eric's kinsmen and

friends were coming with him to settle Greenland. Now it was early summer and the fleet
was sailing out on to the green ocean, headed
for a strange new land in the west. Leif could
hardly keep from yelling with excitement.

"Come here, Thorstein," he called to his
younger brother. "You can still see the mountains of Iceland."

Thorstein came running to stand beside
Leif. A big wave slapped suddenly against the
ship and sent a spray of salt water over them.
The boys laughed and Leif licked the salt water from his lips. Oh, he could never be a
farmer! Sailing was what he wanted to do!

Thorstein, who found it a little hard to
stand up on the rolling deck, went to sit by
Eric.

"Let me steer, Father," he begged.

"Wait till the wind shifts," Eric answered.

"It's hard to keep the course with the wind blowing this way."

Leif, who knew he would have to take a regular turn with the steering, wasn't interested in watching Thorstein do it. He glanced down the ship and saw Tyrker standing near the prow. What was that strange object Tyrker was holding in his hand?

"I'll go see," he told himself.

In order to get to the prow of the ship, Leif had first to jump down into the hold. The ship was long, but it was not very wide. There was a small deck at each end, and under these decks the women slept and much of the provisions were stored.

Along the sides of the ship ran a narrow deck on which were the benches where the rowers sat, two rowers to each bench. Between these rows of benches, in the center of the ship, was the roofless hold. Here the animals were kept, as well as such provisions as could not be hurt by the weather or salt water.

Leif leaped down and landed among some casks and pots. He stepped over these and around a wooden pen full of pigs, who squealed at him hungrily. He walked by the horses, who did not seem to mind the sea voyage. But the sheep and cows looked frightened as they stood huddled together. Leif passed the big wooden block that supported the mast. He looked up at the square sail which hung rather limp, for the wind was not right.

Then he went on past more boxes and bales and two more cows. When Leif had reached the deck in the prow he pulled himself easily up on to it.

Tyrker turned toward him. He was holding a great horn. It was the biggest Leif had ever seen and it was heavily ornamented with gold.

"What kind of horn is that, Tyrker?" Leif asked. "I never saw such a big one."

"It is an aurochs' horn," Tyrker answered.

"An aurochs?" questioned Leif.

"Yes," Tyrker explained. "An aurochs is a great wild ox, much bigger than any tame ox, which roams the forest of my homeland. They are very fierce animals and fight terribly."

Leif was excited. "Do you think there will

be any aurochs or some animal like them in Greenland?" he asked.

Tyrker looked at the boy strangely. "I do not know what animals are found on Greenland. But this I do know. Some of us in this fleet will never see the shores of that new land. I have seen blood on the sun, and it is a bad sign."

He swung himself suddenly down into the hold and disappeared among the baggage. Leif stood looking after him with a strange feeling under his belt. This was a dangerous voyage, he knew. Did Tyrker mean that Eric's dragon ship would sink? Was Tyrker trying to warn him that all those on board were death-marked?

By nightfall Leif had forgotten Tyrker's prediction. Life aboard ship was too new and exciting. Though Leif had often been sailing, he had never before sailed straight out from the land into an unknown sea.

The day passed quickly. He went to sleep on the lower deck near the animals, curling up in his leather sleeping bag with the rowers. His mother and brothers and the women thralls slept under the deck at the rear.

The next day Leif and Thorstein helped to

feed hay to the horses, sheep, and cattle in the hold of the ship. The women thralls milked the cows. The boys drank some of the warm milk from the wooden bucket.

"Sailing makes me hungry," Thorstein said, lifting the bucket again.

Leif passed a bucket of milk and a wooden cup to the rowers, walking along in the hold where the rowers' feet were on a level with his shoulders.

"Ho, Leif!" cried Becan from his bench. "Don't let those others drink it all. I am the best rower on shipboard and I need drink."

"Hush, or we'll throw you overboard," answered another oarsman.

Leif grinned at them. When breakfast was over, he went to the front of the ship and looked off across the water. He would like to be the first to spy Greenland. But he saw nothing except the thin line of the horizon to the west.

He moved about the boat restlessly, glad that he was not seasick like two of the thralls. The steady rise and fall did not bother him in the least. He was a real Viking.

Suddenly he remembered the new sword Eric had given him just before they sailed. He should be wearing it. But where was it? It must be stored under the deck at the prow.

He turned to go under the deck.

"Where are you going?" Thorvald called.

"Just in here to get something. Come with me," Leif answered. He smiled at his youngest brother.

It was easy for Thorvald to go in this space under the deck, but Leif had to stoop. Here all kinds of boxes, bags, bales, and chests were lashed to the beams. Cheeses and bread and grain were wrapped in watertight skin bags. Iron cooking-pots filled with other cooking utensils squatted at the farthest part of the storage place. Leif smiled at the wealth of goods and provisions crowded in this small space.

There were other chests filled with clothes and jewelry. Bales of leather were piled beside a bundle of bridles and harnesses. Bars of iron were tied in place at one side beside an anvil and leather bellows.

"What's in this big chest?" asked Thorvald.

"All the weapons," Leif answered. "I guess Tyrker put my sword in there, too."

He opened the chest and there lay his new sword in a wooden scabbard. It had a two-

*He opened the chest and there lay
his new sword*

edged iron blade and was the best he had ever owned. He proudly buckled the sword and scabbard around his waist.

"I wish I had a sword," Thorvald said wistfully.

"You will some day," Leif promised. "Now get out."

Thorvald rushed out, knocking the wooden bailing scoops from their places. Leif grinned at his brother. Thorvald was as headlong as he had been when he was younger. They put the scoops back in place. Leif hoped the seas wouldn't get so rough that they would have to bail water from the boat with those scoops. They were so small. It made his back ache to think of how many times he'd have to stoop over to fill one of them with water.

He blinked as they stepped outside into the bright summer sunshine.

"Leif," called Eric. "It's your turn at the tiller."

Leif's heart quickened. He loved to take the tiller and sit with the salt wind in his face and the spray blowing around him. He loved to feel the ship move to every turn of the rudder.

Leif climbed to the poop deck at the rear and went to the starboard side. Eric got up from the steersman's seat, still holding the handle of the tiller. Leif eased into his place. His hand closed over the smooth, worn handle. Eric let go and the boy could feel the waters pull at the steering blade.

"Keep her to the southwest, Leif," Eric commanded. "We're sailing around the end of Greenland. If we went straight west, we'd hit ice as I did three years ago. Have you got your bearings by the sun?"

Leif nodded. "Yes, Father," he answered, as he squinted up at the sun. After Eric left the poop deck, Leif wondered if he was too far to the west. Maybe he had better swing the ship's prow a little more to the south. He moved the handle away from him and felt the ship turn toward the left, or south.

He smiled. The gulls wheeled over the ship, screaming their high-pitched calls. The ship rolled and dipped and its dragon head gleamed in the sun.

The striped red and white sail flapped over his head as a quick breeze sprang up. The gold thread which his mother had worked into a design around the edges of the heavy cloth shone brightly. The proud dragon at the prow snarled wonderfully. The rowers kept up their steady rhythm and the oars squeaked in the oarlocks.

Leif took a deep breath and dropped one hand to his sword hilt. This was his boat. He was Leif Ericson, a Viking chieftain, going exploring to strange faraway lands. What a fine life!

A few days later Leif sat with Thorstein at the front of the ship. The rowers were singing an old sea chant as they pulled on the oars.

"How hot the sun is," said Thorstein. "I wish we could jump overboard and take a swim."

"You'd soon get left behind," answered Leif. "The rowers are setting a fast pace."

"Will we reach Greenland soon?"

"I hope so," Leif replied. Suddenly he thought of Tyrker's prophecy, that some of the ships would not reach the new land. There had been no trouble so far. Perhaps if they reached Greenland very soon, they would avoid misfortune. He gave a little shiver. What was it Tyrker had said about a bloody sun? It made him cold all over just to think about it.

Prickles of cold ran up his arms and legs. He *was* cold. The air was cold. He jumped up. What was happening? What had become of the warm brightness of a few minutes ago?

"Leif!" cried Thorstein. "Look at the fog!"

Leif turned quickly. A white wall of fog moved swiftly toward them. The sky was blotted out. The air was clammy and cold as ice. The sea which had been smoothly rolling a few minutes before had become so rough that the rowers pulled their oars into the boat, no longer able to row. The ship swayed in the high wind.

"It's witchcraft," wailed a woman thrall from the hold below.

"Thor protect us!" cried another.

"Keep quiet," bellowed Eric from the steering seat. "It's nothing but fog. Haven't you seen fog before?"

One of the rowers near Leif muttered to his companion, "I never saw fog and cold come on so suddenly in June before."

Suddenly there was a reddish glow around them.

"Look at the sun," shouted someone. "There's blood on it!"

"Ohhhh, we're death-fated!" moaned one of the thralls. "It's an evil omen!"

Leif glanced up. The sun shone through the fog, round as a shield and as red as blood spill-

ing from a death wound. Tyrker's prophecy
was coming true!

"Leif, I'm scared," said Thorstein as he
grabbed his brother's hand.

There was a roar as a huge wave came toward them and struck the ship. The boys staggered with the impact. The sheep bleated piti-
fully. A thrall tried to quiet the horses.
"Whoa, there, Big Red! Whoa!"

A horse gave a wild neigh and the terrified
cattle bellowed. Another huge wave suddenly
swept over the ship. Leif held on to Thorstein.
For a moment he thought they were both going to be swept overboard.

"The scoops!" Becan shouted. "Get the

bailing scoops! The hold is filling with water!"

"Tyrker, get the rowers to bailing," ordered Eric.

The hold was a mass of milling men and animals. The women thralls moaned and cried out from under decks, in fear. "We'll be drowned. The ship's bewitched!"

Leif tugged at his brother. "Get into the hold, Thorstein," he shouted. He lowered his brother from the foredeck. As he did so, he saw the horn where it hung on a peg, knocking against the side of the ship. He had a sudden inspiration. He grabbed the aurochs' horn from the wooden peg. He would blow it so the rest of the fleet would know where Eric's dragon ship was.

He put the horn to his lips and blew.

"That's it. Keep blowing," yelled Eric. "We'll keep the ships together, anyway!"

Leif blew with all his might. There was a sudden angry rush of waves. The ship lurched beneath the force of the water. Leif felt himself lifted into the air from the deck and hurtled over the gunwale. The wave had washed him off the ship! He felt the rough water close over his head. Down he sank into the dark, cold ocean!

CHAPTER EIGHT

Greenland at Last

LEIF came to the surface of the water gasping for breath. He could just make out the dark shape of the ship through the fog. He struck out toward it, but the great waves tossed him about. He'd never been in such rough water. It was useless to try to swim. A huge wave carried him up until he could look down on the deck. He tried to call for help, but salt water filled his mouth.

Then he was whirled down, down, into the trough of a wave. The shadowy ship towered over him. For a minute he thought the ship would be washed down on him. He shouted desperately for help, but then another wave carried the ship away. He was afraid the ship would vanish out of sight in the fog.

Once more he tried to swim through the

He was whirled down into the trough of a wave

rolling ocean. But it was useless. It was all he could do to hold his head above the water. If someone didn't help him soon, he would be lost. He would surely drown.

Through the noise of the storm he thought he heard someone call his name. Something fell into the water near him. Was it a rope?

He stretched out his arms, feeling frantically in the water. Once he thought his fingers touched the rope, then it was gone. He couldn't find it anywhere.

A wave broke over his head and filled his nose and mouth with water. He choked and felt himself begin to sink. At that moment something slapped him in the face. It was the rope! Joyfully he seized it. He shut his eyes and held on with all his strength, as he was pulled toward the ship.

The waves tugged at him and he felt as if his arms were being pulled from their sockets, but he held on. In a few minutes he was hauled to the deck. Tyrker pounded him on the back.

"Thanks be to Thor, he hasn't swallowed too much water," the German said.

"I'm all right," Leif gasped. "What has happened, Tyrker? Is it witchcraft?"

"I don't know," answered Tyrker. "But I've

never witnessed such a strange thing before in my life."

All that day the boats tossed about in the rough waters and fog. At sunset the fog cleared and the water became calmer. Eric and Tyrker peered anxiously across the ocean, looking for the others in the fleet. By nightfall twenty battered ships had gathered together. Some had broken masts, others had their sails hanging in tatters.

"Where are the other five?" asked Thorstein.

"Lost," Tyrker answered. "Lost in that accursed fog. May Odin grant their souls rest."

Five days later the little fleet approached Greenland. There were only fourteen ships following Eric now, for six had returned to Iceland. Their chiefs had been afraid to sail on after the sudden storm, which had seemed to them an ill omen.

Leif and Thorstein were glad to see land. After the storm the ships had encountered icebergs as well as strange currents and dangerous reefs. And now all on board were glad to be nearing the end of the voyage.

As they approached closer to Greenland, the other ships left them, each chieftain going to

Finally only Eric's ship was left

seek a homeplace of his own. Finally only Eric's ship was left sailing up a fiord.

Thorstein ran from one side of the boat to the other. "Look at the mountains, Leif," he cried excitedly. "Leif, see the geese flying overhead! They are different from the geese in Iceland."

Leif laughed. "I see you're going to fall overboard if you don't calm down." He watched the big white birds flying over the green mountains. "How green the land is! No wonder Father called it Greenland."

"There it is!" suddenly shouted Eric. "There's the site I've picked for our farm. We'll build the hall right by the spring."

Leif looked toward the sloping hillside where his father pointed. So this was going to be his new home. He tried to picture the green slopes dotted with farm buildings as Ox Island had been. Would the cattle barns go there and the storerooms yonder? He hoped the feasting hall would be as fine as the one at home. He could hardly wait to land.

A week later there was no need to puzzle over where the buildings would be located. The stone foundations for barns and outbuildings had been laid. And the sod house where

Leif was to live was going up fast. The turf was cut in strips and laid on the stone foundation. The roots of weeds and grasses held the earth together. After the dirt was wetted and packed, the walls would keep out the wind and weather very well.

Thorvald and Thorstein liked Greenland very much. After the cramped days on board ship they enjoyed running on the grassy meadows along the fiord. They chased lemmings and climbed among the rocks along the shore, hunting for the eggs of the great auk and other sea birds. They played in the dwarf willow and birch trees along the creek banks. These shrubby trees were the only trees in Greenland and seldom grew higher than a man's head.

Leif had less time to play and explore. He was busy the whole day helping to lay the strips of sod on the rock foundations. He was a little disappointed in this new land. It was not so strange after all. Here were the same green meadows and snow-topped mountains he remembered in Iceland. But Eric had told him of icy fields to the north where caribou could be found—and polar bears and other animals that Leif had never seen. Leif was anxious to complete the houses so he could go hunting.

He led her to the rear of the house

One day as he was piling up the sod blocks which the thralls brought him, his father and mother walked up from the ship.

Thorhild inspected the building with a look of discontent. "The work is going very well, Leif," she said. Then she turned to Eric. "But it worries me that the hall will be so small and have walls made only of dirt. It isn't fitting for the leader of the Greenland settlers to live in such a place."

"We must do the best we can with what we have at hand," Eric answered in a soothing tone. "We have no wood. A stone house would require too many fires to keep it warm. The sod houses will keep us warm and dry until we can send a ship to Iceland for wood. We might even send to Norway for wood."

He took his wife by the arm and gently led her to the rear of the house.

"There," he pointed. "There is something we didn't have in Iceland. Water right inside the house."

Near the corner of the house a spring bubbled out of the earth. The water flowed in a rock-lined trench under the rear wall and into the house. There it fell into a basin. The overflow ran off in another rock channel.

"We will cover the ditch and basin with flat rocks," Eric told her. "And when you want water, you'll only have to lift the stone and dip it out. Is that not better than bringing water daily into the hall from a springhouse?"

Thorhild laughed. "Yes, that will be a great convenience," she said. "When we build a fine new hall of wood we'll build it right here and use the spring just like this."

"Good," Eric exclaimed. "This is a fine site for a house. And our sod home will soon be finished. By winter the barns and sheds will be completed. Leif, you've worked well. Take the ship's boat now, and go with your brothers to search for driftwood. Any piece of wood you find can be used, no matter how small."

Leif needed no urging. He dropped a last strip of sod in place and ran toward the shore. He was always glad to go out in a boat. He was glad, too, to hear Eric say that the houses and barns would be finished before winter. Leif was anxious to get settled so he could go exploring this new land. Who knew what riches lay back among the icy mountains of Greenland?

CHAPTER NINE

The Walrus Hunt

A YEAR later the Greenland colonists were well settled into their new life. Eric's farm was completed, with barns, storehouses, temple, smithy, and other buildings. The houses of stone and sod no longer looked strange to Leif. The countryside, too, had become familiar to him, for he had hunted and explored over much of the surrounding area.

Now that he was fourteen, Leif had to take over much of the management of the farm work. One summer day he and Eric climbed the slope of the mountain that loomed behind the Greenland farm. Halfway up Eric stopped and said, "This is the place where I want to build a new shelter for the sheep herders. Bring two thralls tomorrow and begin work. Don't spend too much time on it, for the shelter will only be used in the summer when the sheep graze here."

Leif said nothing. He was staring out across the sea.

"Leif, did you hear a word I said?" Eric asked.

The boy gave a start. "I'm sorry, Father," he said. "I was thinking of the good time Tyrker and I had up the coast last month when we were hunting. You know I really like sailing and exploring much better than farming."

Eric laughed. "You are a real Viking," he admitted. "But Viking days are over for us. Very few go sea-roving these days. And here in Greenland especially, we need more farmers than sailors. I'm getting old, you know." He indicated the valley below with a sweep of his hand. "You'll have to take over all of this one of these days."

"I know, Father," Leif nodded. "I love the farm and I mean to take care of it as well as I am able. But before that day comes I would like to ride a dragon far off toward the west . . ." He broke off suddenly and stared off toward the sea. "Isn't that a ship coming into the fiord?" he asked.

*"Isn't that a ship coming into
the fiord?" he asked*

"Your eyes are better than mine. I see nothing," answered Eric. "But I hope it's a trading ship."

They watched a moment in silence. Then Eric exclaimed, "Yes, I see it now. Let's hurry home and see who it is."

They started down the mountain and Leif's heart pounded with excitement. Who was this stranger coming up the fiord?

But it turned out not to be a stranger at all. It was Bjarni Herjulfson, whom they had known in Iceland. He was a famous trader. His father had come to Greenland with Eric and had settled not far away.

That night as they sat in the feast hall Bjarni told Eric what he had come for. He had spent the winter with his father, Herjulf, and had found Greenland very much to his liking. "I am a wealthy man," he said. "I have done enough trading and I want to settle down. I would like to take land near my father."

Eric did not own the land in Greenland, but all the settlers looked upon him as their official leader. He allotted the land and settled all disputes.

Eric was delighted to have a new settler. He knew that Bjarni was a fine man and would make a good citizen. In a few minutes they had settled the details of what lands Bjarni was to have and how much.

"My father will be delighted that I have land adjoining his," Bjarni said. "Now can you tell me any other news to take him?"

"But you are the one who has news for us," cried Eric. "What is this rumor we hear that you sighted lands to the west of here?"

Leif, who had been playing a game of chess with Tyrker, sprang up and came to Bjarni's side. "Is it *really* true, Bjarni, that you found land? One of our thralls told us it was the gossip at Einar's hall."

Bjarni laughed and answered, "Yes it's true. But I wish I had never told the tale. It has earned me more blame than honor. You see, when I sailed from Norway to spend the winter with my father, I did not know he had left Iceland and come here with you, Eric. I landed in Iceland and found he had gone. So I did not even unload my boat, but left straightaway for Greenland. I had only vague directions about how to reach this land. But my rowers were brave and willing to risk it, even though it was so near winter."

Leif smiled. He hoped the day he went ex-

[*99*]

ploring, his oarsmen would be as brave and as loyal as Bjarni's.

"We put to sea and sailed for three days," Bjarni went on. "Then we were beset by fogs and north winds until we lost our course. When the sun came out so we could get our bearings, we set sail toward the north.

"After a day we sighted land. But it did not fit the descriptions I had heard of Greenland, for it was covered with small wooded knolls. We left that land behind and sailed in a north-easterly direction and twice more sighted land. Then we sailed on and finally arrived here safely."

"Didn't you land anywhere?" asked Leif in astonishment.

"No," answered Bjarni. "It was too late in the winter. I wanted to hurry to Greenland before the ice formed in the fiords. Now some people say I was a fool for sailing from Iceland with such poor sailing directions. And others say I was stupid not to have stopped and explored the new lands." He laughed again. "So you see why I wish I had not told this story."

Leif was silent. He, too, thought Bjarni was foolish for not having brought back more information about the new country.

"You were right not to risk your ship," Eric reassured his guest. "A ship is too hard to replace here in Greenland."

"Don't you ever plan to go back to those western lands, Bjarni?" asked Leif.

Bjarni shook his head. "I'm through with sailing," he said.

Then he and Eric began to discuss how trade between Iceland and Greenland could be increased. But Leif was not listening. He was dreaming of those lands to the west.

As the years passed, Leif went on dreaming, but he could not go exploring. Life was hard for the people in the Greenland colony. Young and able-bodied men like Leif were always busy working to produce the many things which the colonists needed. Leif could not be spared to go a-voyaging.

Besides, there were few ships on Greenland. There was no wood available to build new ships. And the people needed those they had for trading and fishing expeditions.

Leif came to know well the reasons why he could not go exploring. But he did not give up hope. He had grown into a thoughtful man. He was respected among the Greenlanders, not only because he was Red Eric's son, but because he was intelligent and hard working. And he was carefully laying plans for the future.

For the next seven years Leif worked on the farm and went hunting and fishing. He was an expert huntsman. He hunted caribou, walruses, seals, and musk-oxen. The meat from these animals provided food for his family. Their hides and the walrus tusks were saved to be traded in Norway and Iceland for things which the colony needed.

Part of the hides and tusks which were saved each year belonged to Leif. But he did not trade them for other goods. He sold them for gold which he carefully saved. And he told no one what he intended to do with it.

One day in late fall, after his twenty-first birthday, Leif sailed from his home with Tyrker and several thralls for a hunting expedition. The party was in Eric's small boat, for the long dragon ship had been beached for the winter in a shed beside the fiord. Besides, the smaller boat was easier to handle among the rocks and ice along the dangerous eastern coast of Greenland, where Leif liked to hunt.

The thralls rowed the boat from Eric's

fiord, and Leif guided it south and around Greenland's southernmost point of land. Sailing north along the eastern coast a few days later, Leif steered carefully in and out of the bays, his eyes scanning the rocky cliffs for game.

By the end of the week the boat was piled with the skins and meat.

"Let's turn back," suggested Tyrker. "We have killed enough, Leif." He glanced up. "Those clouds will bring snow and ice."

Leif looked at the line of gray clouds moving toward them from the northeast. The wind was rising. The leaden sky looked sullen.

Leif laughed. He turned to Tyrker and said, "Foster father, we've hunted much later in the year than this. You're getting old. You like the feast-hall fire more than you used to." He pointed toward the middle of the boat where the skins and meat lay. "There's not much walrus ivory there. We'll sail a little way north to where the ice pushes into the sea. Walruses are sure to be there."

Tyrker shrugged his shoulders and wrapped a long woolen cloak around himself. He sat down near Leif and stared pensively at the coastline of Greenland.

The high mountains, covered with snow and glacial ice, were blanketed in fog. Over the tall, rocky cliffs sea birds circled in the wind. Several queer-looking shaggy forms grazed among the rocks.

"Musk-ox," Tyrker called. He pointed to the strange beasts with their curious horns.

Leif shook his head. He wanted walrus ivory. He would not hunt musk-ox today.

For an hour the rowers kept up a steady rhythm. The boat rode smoothly in the dark green water. Once a whale broke the surface in front of their boat. It shot a stream of water into the air from its blow hole and disappeared. The spray blew in their faces.

At last Leif said, "Here, take the tiller, Tyrker. I will go to the prow to watch for hidden rocks."

Tyrker slid into the steersman's seat and Leif pointed ahead. "Steer for that opening in the ice," he said. "That'll be a good place to get walruses."

Leif went forward and leaned out, searching for the dark water that meant hidden reefs ahead. Tyrker followed Leif's directions and the boat moved into calmer water.

Glistening walls of ice towered over them.

The sea had eaten into the glacier, making a cave of crystal ice. Tyrker steered among the pillars and corridors. Green and blue lights played along the smooth walls and in and out of the crevices and crannies which the waves had carved in the huge block of ice.

Leif scanned the pockets and ice flats for animals. Then he spotted a walrus sleeping on a shelf of ice that stuck out into the bay. He pointed out the animal to Tyrker and got his bow and arrow ready.

As the German guided the boat close beside the shelf, Leif pulled the notched arrow back until its feathered end touched his cheek. He aimed and shot. The arrow sank into the walrus' creased neck.

Quickly Leif grabbed two spears and jumped to the shelf. The wounded walrus turned on its assailant, bellowing fiercely. It raised its big head. The two long tusks pointed at Leif. Then it charged furiously across the ice. Blood flowed from the wound in its neck and made a red trail across the icy shelf.

Leif threw a heavy iron-pointed spear into the huge body. The walrus stopped and shook itself and roared again. The sound echoed in the cave and a huge piece of ice dropped from

Quickly Leif grabbed two spears

the glacier wall and splashed into the bay.

Leif moved forward carefully but quickly and shoved his other spear into the animal's throat. With an awkward twisting of its head the walrus slumped to the ice, dead. Leif placed his spear beside him and set to work to skin the walrus.

Gulls suddenly began to whirl close around his head. They screamed as they flew by. Leif knew that when he had finished with the walrus they would eat what was left. Gulls and foxes and wolves always ate the left-over meat.

Suddenly Tyrker's voice came across the ice to him, "Leif! Look out! A bear!"

Leif was on his feet at once with his bloody knife in his hand. He looked up into the snarling open jaws of a polar bear. The white animal reared above him on its hind legs. Its small black eyes squinted. A growl came from deep in its chest.

The bear was so close that Leif could not get away. He had only one chance with his knife. Quickly he struck for the bear's throat. But the bear was quicker. Its sharp claws raked along Leif's arm and hand, tearing away the knife and leaving the flesh in ribbons. And Leif faced the bear unarmed.

CHAPTER TEN

Off to Norway

THE bear towered over Leif on its hind legs. Its black jaws and gleaming teeth dripped hot saliva. With a rumbling roar of triumph, the bear lunged for the Viking. Leif took a quick step backward and stumbled over the dead walrus. His feet went out from under him and he hit the ice with a jarring thud. He lay breathless on his back, looking straight up at the huge beast.

Leif could hear the others shouting as they made their way over the ice toward him. But he knew they would be too late to save him. He had to get away from the bear without their help.

He threw out his hands in an effort to raise himself from the ice. His fingers touched the wooden shaft of his spear. In an instant he

[*108*]

raised the spear point, bracing the end of the shaft against the ice. At the same time the great body of the bear fell toward him.

For a minute Leif thought that he had raised the spear too late to stop the bear, and that he would be killed. Then the point tore into the white chest. He felt the weapon tremble. The wooden shaft began to bend under the weight of the animal. Swiftly Leif rolled away.

The shaft was splintered. The bear bellowed horribly as it fell to the ground with the broken spear impaled in its chest. Red blood spurted out across the ice.

The bear was not yet dead. With hideous roars and grunts it raised itself and crawled toward Leif. Its black eyes sparkled with rage and hate. Leif was too stunned and dizzy from his fall to run. He moved slowly backward from the wounded bear, step by step.

Tyrker and the thralls came running up. They stuck their spears into the bear's body. The light went from its eyes. Its white form slumped dead to the ice.

"Are you hurt, foster son?" panted Tyrker.

"No," Leif answered. "Skin the beast," he ordered the thralls.

The thralls hesitated. Tyrker gave Leif an odd look.

"Eric won't like this, Leif," he said. "You

know he regards these white bears as sacred. He says they are our brothers."

Leif laughed. "He came close to losing his son to this one," he answered. "Eric won't

know about it. I'll hide the white fur among
my own furs and skins."

The thralls set to work while Tyrker took

Leif to one side to bind up the cuts which the
bear had made in his arm.

"You must sacrifice to Thor tonight," Tyrker told Leif. "You can deceive Eric about

the bear, but you cannot deceive the gods. Who knows, perhaps the white bears *are* sacred."

Leif sighed. "Very well," he answered. "But I tell you truly, Tyrker, there are times when I wonder whether the gods pay any heed to sacrifices. There are times when I feel in my heart that Odin and Thor and the other gods do not exist at all."

Tyrker looked shocked. "Leif, how can you say such things? Did I not pray for our hunting to be successful? And have you ever seen more skins or finer ones?"

Leif looked toward the boat where the furs were piled. "Yes, they are fine skins," he admitted. "My share will be a big one."

Tyrker leaned toward Leif and looked at him earnestly. "My son, why are you so anxious for hides?" he asked. "Why do you risk your life for another piece of walrus ivory? All you ever take from the traders is gold. And what use is gold in Greenland?"

"Do you remember how you used to scold me when I was a boy for rushing into things without planning ahead?" Leif asked his foster father. "Well, I no longer do that. I lay my plans as carefully as I can. Now I am planning to go west, to the lands Bjarni Herjulfson saw. I have no ship. Eric would not give me his dragon for such a voyage. So, for seven years, I have saved my gold.

"Soon I will have enough to buy a ship of my own. Then I will sail west. I will not be afraid to land, as Bjarni was. I will plan wisely and take proper provisions. I will go ashore on those strange lands and explore them from end to end."

Tyrker was silent for a long time. At last he spoke. "I know that you will do what you say you will, Leif. You are strong and brave. But there is much danger ahead of you. I will pray that the gods will protect you."

Five more years went by. The Greenland colonies were not yet as prosperous as Eric had hoped they would be. Ships did not come often enough from Norway and Iceland to bring the things the Greenlanders needed. They were in special need of iron and wheat. Some of the poorer children born on Greenland had never tasted bread, because grain was so scarce.

It took Leif longer than he had expected to save enough money for a ship. But finally he had the amount he needed. One night he took

[*113*]

his gold from the chest where he had kept it locked and went in search of his father. Eric was in the feasting hall. But he was not sitting in the high seat. He was sitting on a bench drawn close to the fire, talking to Thorhild. Thorhild was spinning. Leif stood watching the spindle fly between his mother's fingers and listening to his parents' voices.

Finally he stepped forward into the fire-light. A little table stood near Eric. Without saying anything, Leif went to the table and poured out his gold. It made a shimmering heap and one piece fell to the floor and rolled under Eric's bench.

Eric jumped up. "What in the name of Odin is this?" he cried.

Leif stooped and picked up the gold piece. "This is my new boat, Father," he answered. "As soon as the weather is warm enough, I mean to go to Bjarni Herjulfson and buy his ship. He is willing to sell it. I am going to sea, to explore the lands Bjarni saw in the west. I have saved this money, to buy my own ship so that I would not need to use your dragon. Thorstein is able to take care of the farm and help you. There is nothing to stop me now."

Leif had expected his father to be angry or

to argue with him. Instead, Eric answered quietly, "Very well, Leif. But before you go sea-roving there is one thing I would like you to do for me. It is fitting that the eldest son of Greenland's chief should be presented at court. I want you to go to Norway to pledge allegiance to King Olaf, as all young Vikings should. At his court you will meet many rich and influential men. They may be a help to you in many ways. But I want you to go for another reason."

He paused and looked into the fire. Leif thought he looked a little sad. "Greenland must have iron and wheat and lumber," Eric went on. "We must have more trade with Norway. I want you to persuade the King to send trading vessels here. I want you to get some rich man to send us iron and lumber in exchange for hides and ivory."

"I'll go, Father," Leif said. "I'll leave as soon as the ice begins to clear in the spring."

It took a good many days to get ready for the voyage. The dragon ship was repaired carefully. Provisions for the journey were stored in the hold, along with a supply of skins and hides to be traded. At last came the day for departure. Leif and his family went into the temple. There Eric sacrificed a horse, for it was the custom to offer a horse to the gods before a journey.

Kettle the Black, whose family had moved to Greenland, was to make the journey with Leif. Finally all was ready. Kettle and Leif boarded the ship. The anchor was drawn up, and down the fiord they sailed and out into the ocean.

"Now let us set our course for Iceland," said Kettle. Ships sailed from Greenland to Iceland and then to Norway. In this way they did not have to sail far from land on the whole journey.

"No," Leif replied. "Not for Iceland—for Norway."

"What do you mean?" asked Kettle.

"I mean," said Leif calmly, "to sail straight out across the ocean and reach Norway without stopping!"

CHAPTER ELEVEN

The Berserker's Challenge

IT WAS a beautiful summer afternoon when Leif steered the dragon ship up the fiord toward Nidaros, Norway. Kettle the Black stood beside him. "You are a great navigator, Leif," he said. "I never thought the journey from Greenland to Norway could be made without stopping at Iceland."

"I was sure it could be done," answered Leif. "I had talked about it to many old sailors. I figured that if I sailed due east from the southern tip of Greenland and then between the Faroë and Shetland Islands, I would reach Norway safely."

Kettle clapped his hand on Leif's shoulder. "Well, I see you were right," he exclaimed. "By Thor, Leif, look at the ships in this harbor! Greenland could use a few of these."

Leif looked around at the ships. There were many different kinds—fishing boats, trading vessels, and warships. Greenland could use more ships, Leif thought, but not ships like some of these. They looked so heavy and awkward that he knew they could not be used in the shallow water of the fiords. He thought they must come from foreign countries.

"Look, yonder is a place to tie up," Kettle said, pointing to a space between the ships.

Skillfully, Leif maneuvered his dragon ship into place. A thrall made the craft fast.

Kettle glanced at the sun. "It's too late to try to see King Olaf today, Leif. Let us go ashore and look around. Tomorrow we can present ourselves at court."

Leif gave orders to the thralls to put the ship in order. Then he and Kettle prepared to go ashore.

Six of the oarsmen were not thralls, but sons of Greenland's chieftains. They had volunteered to go with Leif in order to be presented at court. These young men came ashore with Leif and Kettle. All eight began to look around at the strange sights.

"Look, Leif," cried Kettle. "Look at the great dragon ship being built over there!"

The group made their way toward the almost completed boat. Leif gave a whistle. "That's the longest ship I've ever seen," he remarked.

One of the workmen spoke up proudly. "It's almost two hundred feet long and belongs to King Olaf Tryggvason."

"I would most certainly like to steer that one," Leif said.

They walked on among the tents and wooden booths of merchants and traders. There were tables piled high with strange wares. Here was a man selling raisins, dates, sweetmeats, and wines. The air was filled with their fragrance.

Now a man began to cry his wares, holding up a cage containing a bright red bird. "Singing birds and peacocks! Buy a fine peafowl!"

Leif remembered the peacock he had seen at Egil the Bellower's in Iceland. He looked at the peacocks and the cages full of other brilliantly colored birds, but he did not buy.

Over there was a merchant selling bronze and silver necklaces and bracelets. The Greenlanders elbowed their way through the throng to see his display. A man passed them dressed in a long, bright-colored robe. On his head he wore a red turban and from his bright sash hung a curious curved sword. But to Leif the strangest things about him were his dark brown skin and great black eyes.

Behind the brown-skinned man came other men also dressed in flowing robes, but these robes were white. The men wore their hair cut short. Around their necks were necklaces from which dangled gold crosses.

The Greenlanders watched them pass in silence. Leif was curious about them. He stopped a passer-by.

"Who are those fellows?" he asked, pointing to the white-robed figures.

"Why, they are Irish priests," the man answered him. He made the sign of the cross on his chest. "They are Christians. We are all Christians here now. And yonder is the fine new church that King Olaf has built."

He pointed to a great wooden building. On the roof was a large gold cross. The Greenlanders had heard of the White Christ and His Cross, but never before had they seen one of His temples. Leif and the others stared up.

The setting sun gleamed on the cross.

"It is late," said Leif. "Let us return to the ship."

As he turned in the crowd, Leif bumped against a big man who was finely dressed in silk shirt and breeches. In his belt he wore a jeweled sword and on his head a close-fitting helmet with ox horns attached at the sides. His shield was highly decorated.

The man shoved against Leif and cried, "You clumsy fool! Don't you know that all men make way for Gest Olafson, the Berserker?"

Leif stared into the ugly scarred face with its cruel little eyes. This was indeed his old enemy. He remembered his fight with Gest at the feast, and Tyrker's warning that they would always be enemies. And now it seemed that Gest wanted to fight again.

"Leif Ericson gives way to no man," Leif replied coolly as he stood his ground.

Gest went red with anger. Kettle pulled Leif's arm. "Come away quickly before he challenges you," he said in a low voice. "He is a champion Berserker. If you refuse to fight, he is entitled to all your property. That is the law!"

"I challenge you!" the Berserker cried. "And I wager a hundred pieces of gold against your ship and goods."

"It was not I who sought out this fight," Leif answered boldly. "But I will not refuse your challenge."

In his heart, however, he trembled. Could he really defeat this more experienced fighter? He knew that a Berserker made his living by challenging other men. When he won a fight, the Berserker was entitled to whatever part of his opponent's property had been wagered.

Sometimes men were so afraid of Berserkers that they refused to fight. Then they forfeited everything they owned to the Berserker who had challenged them. Because of their cruelty and bad tempers, the Berserkers were much feared and disliked.

Leif thought of the load of skins that Eric had sent to be traded for lumber. He thought of Eric's beautiful dragon ship. If he lost the fight, all would go to Gest Olafson. He *couldn't* lose. He *had* to win this battle.

A crowd gathered around him and Gest in the twilight. The Berserker began to tremble and gnash his teeth. His head shook violently. He lifted his shield and bit it in fury.

"He's working himself up into a Berserk rage," Kettle said as he took Leif's spear and scabbard.

Leif went on calmly preparing himself for battle. "It won't help him," he remarked. "He'll feel the bite of my sword." He slipped his shield on his left arm and stepped forward to meet Gest.

The Berserker was foaming at the mouth. His body jerked and shook. Suddenly with a wild cry he flung away his shield and charged Leif. His sword whirred through the air. Leif met the blow with his shield. Gest's blade cut through the wooden shield and into Leif's arm.

[*123*]

With a wild cry he charged Leif

Leif threw his useless shield aside. Blood trickled down his arm, but the wound was not serious.

Gest gave a triumphant cry at the sight of blood and rushed Leif again. With his sword he hacked back and forth at the Greenlander.

Leif ducked the blow at his head. He moved backward from the body cut. As Gest swung the blade at his legs, he leaped into the air. The sword swished furiously under his up-drawn feet.

It was growing darker. Gest's blade flew back and forth in powerful arcs.

Leif moved forward as if to meet the attack. An instant later he sidestepped and at the same time hacked at Gest's legs. He made a deep cut across the Berserker's thigh. Leif had heard that Berserkers could not be harmed by an iron sword. Now he learned this was not true, for blood gushed from the wound. Nevertheless, Gest seemed to feel no pain. He did not seem to know he had been injured.

The Berserker attacked again.

Again Leif leaped a blow, jumping high into the air and striking at the Berserker's neck. There was a shout from Leif's friends as his blade found its mark. Leif laughed aloud. He knew now that he was the better fighter and that he would win.

The Berserker stopped and shook his head. Blood flowed across his bare chest. Leif pressed his advantage and attacked quickly. A blow aimed at the other's legs caused Gest to lower his sword hurriedly to meet the blow. As he did so, Leif struck the side of the Berserker's head. Gest fell to the ground, stunned.

A cheer went up from the crowd.

Leif turned to Kettle and took his scabbard and spear.

The Greenlanders moved off through the admiring crowd.

"Let us go back to our ship," Leif said quietly. "Now there is one less Berserker to plunder innocent men. For I think Gest Olafson will never fight again."

CHAPTER TWELVE

A Promise

THE city of Nidaros was only two years old. The streets were muddy paths. There were few houses or buildings, for most of the traders and visitors lived in tents or temporary wooden huts. Nevertheless, the city was thronged with people. A great many of these were attached to King Olaf's court. These king's men were beautifully dressed in silks and furs and wore many handsome bracelets and jewels.

Leif had known that this would be so. He had realized that the Greenlanders would look rough and poorly dressed compared to the fine courtiers. But Leif did not want King Olaf to think of the Greenlanders as poor, uncouth men. So he had planned a new kind of dress for his party.

The following morning as the eight young men walked toward the King's hall, every eye turned toward them. Each man was dressed in a jacket of polar bear fur with a hood made from the bear's head. Each Greenlander looked out from under the black snout and gleaming teeth of a polar bear. And on each man's wrist sat one of the much-prized white falcons of Greenland. These falcons were to be a gift to King Olaf Tryggvason.

The Greenlanders made their way through the admiring throng outside Olaf's feasting hall. This was the biggest and finest building Leif had ever seen. It was built of wood, for wood was plentiful in Norway, and decorated with a great deal of carving.

"Make way for the Greenlanders!" a soldier shouted.

Someone opened the great door and the eight men entered the hall. The building was filled with noise and confusion. Men were everywhere and thralls ran to and fro.

Leif led his companions through the crowd toward the King. King Olaf sat in his high seat talking to the people around him. They turned to stare at the newcomers. Suddenly the falcon on Leif's wrist gave a high, rattling scream, easily heard over the noise of the hall. Now even King Olaf turned to look.

The crowd parted and Leif stood before the King. He saluted Olaf and spoke.

"My name is Leif, son of Eric the Red," he said. "We come from Greenland across the sea to bring you gifts and pledge you our allegiance."

The King stood up to receive the gifts. He was a huge man with bright blue eyes and fine features. Leif liked his warm and friendly look. The King seemed pleased with the gifts. Thralls took the falcons away.

"Make yourselves at home," the King said to the Greenlanders. "I will have meat and drink brought for you. And later we will talk. There is much I want to hear about Greenland."

The Greenlanders stayed at King Olaf's court all that fall and winter. They became great favorites of the King, especially Leif.

One afternoon in late fall, King Olaf and Leif went hunting in order that the King might exercise his favorite falcon. There was a small retinue of soldiers and thralls with them. It was a clear cold day. They rode along a steep cliff high above the waters of the fiord.

Suddenly Leif exclaimed, "Yonder goes a plover."

King Olaf unleashed the falcon. He threw up his arm to give the bird a better take-off. The falcon soared into the air and hovered over the yellow-and-white plover. Then it dived toward its prey, but the plover, too, dropped down toward the sea. Twisting aside, it escaped among the rocks and bushes along the cliff wall. The falcon checked itself in mid-air and swerved out over the water. Then suddenly it lighted in a small tree fifty feet below the top of the cliff.

Leif and the King had dismounted and could clearly see the bird below them. King Olaf called to the falcon. The bird spread its wings to fly, but the leather straps around its legs were tangled in the branches.

"The leather jeeses must be caught," Olaf said. He turned to a thrall standing beside them and said, "Nord, fetch me the falcon."

Nord was a small and nimble man. He looked like a good climber, yet he hesitated as he looked at the steep cliff below him. Then with a final glance at the King, he lowered himself carefully over the edge.

Leif watched the thrall going slowly down

the steep cliff face. He searched for each foothold and made his way cautiously toward the
falcon.

"There is a trading ship in the fiord," said
the King. "I hope it's Glint, the trader I sent
to France."

Leif looked toward the west where the King
pointed. He could make out the trading ship
approaching Nidaros.

Suddenly there was a terrified scream from
the cliff below. Leif and Olaf stared down.
The thrall had slid past the falcon and was
hanging to a rock ledge, with his feet kicking
wildly out in space.

"He's fallen!" exclaimed Leif. "Shall I go
down and help him?" he asked the King.

The King looked down at the kicking thrall
and called, "Hang on, Nord. Stop kicking.
I'll come down and get you." He turned to
Leif and handed him his woolen cloak.
"Thank you, Leif, but I sent him down for my
falcon. It is all my doing, so I will go."

Leif watched the King as he quickly lowered
himself over the cliff's edge. Although Olaf
was a tall man, and bigger than Leif, he moved
from rock to rock with lightness and grace.

At last he reached the stunted tree and re-

The thrall was hanging to a rock ledge

leased the falcon. The bird flew off with a scream. The King then lowered himself past the tree to the small ledge from which the thrall hung. Reaching down, he grabbed Nord by the wrists and jerked him up. Now taking the trembling man under his arm, he began to climb back up the cliff.

Leif felt sure he would never make it. It was difficult enough for a man to get only himself from handhold to handhold and footrest to footrest. But to carry someone else up that dangerous rock wall was too much to expect of any man, even a king.

Still Olaf climbed steadily upward. Back and forth across the face of the cliff he moved. The thrall's weight did not seem to bother him at all. Leif had never seen anyone so unconcerned in the face of danger as King Olaf. The thrall, however, hung limp and terrified.

Once Olaf's hand slipped from a crack in the rock. Leif gasped, afraid that both men would be dashed to pieces on the rocks far below. But the moment Olaf's fingers lost their hold, he leaped upward and grabbed a knob of rock above him. He dug his toes into a foothold and continued on upward.

At last the King reached the top and placed the thrall safely on his feet.

"That was a kingly deed, Sire," Leif declared. "I have never seen your equal for strength or daring."

Olaf wiped the sweat from his face and grinned at Leif. "A man must never let his thralls or his falcons die, if he can prevent it," he said, as he put on his cloak. He held up his arm and called to the white bird circling overhead. The falcon fluttered down and lit on the leather band around his wrist.

They mounted their horses and started back toward Nidaros. Along the way the King talked to Leif of his boyhood days, and of his fights in England as a young man. He told him of the many troubles with which he had to deal as ruler of Norway.

"One of my biggest problems, Leif," Olaf said, "was getting the Norse people to accept Christianity. Many of them say that Odin and Thor were good enough for their fathers, and the old religion is still good enough for them."

"We in Greenland follow the old religion," remarked Leif. "My father's belief in Thor is strong."

"Yes, I knew you were Thor's men," Olaf

answered. "I see that you wear Thor's hammer on a chain around your neck."

Leif felt for the necklace he had worn ever since he won it in an archery contest in Iceland as a youth. There was nothing wrong in believing in Thor, Leif thought. Yet a man should be able to choose his religion as he chose his clothes, and change both if he saw fit.

"There are times when I wonder if the old gods have not died," he said at last. "Is it true that the White Christ whom you follow is weaker than Thor? That is what I have heard said."

The King turned on his horse and faced Leif riding beside him. "Leif, do I look like a man who would believe in a weak religion? If I did not think Christ stronger and better than Thor, I would not tell everyone about Him." He slapped his right hand on his leg and went on earnestly, "I tell you the White Christ has more strength than Thor ever dreamed of."

Leif looked at this powerfully built man beside him. "No," he thought to himself, "such a man as King Olaf would not follow a weak god. A man who would walk up a cliff with a thrall under his arm would hardly be satisfied with less than the best.

"Tell me about this White Christ of yours, Sire," Leif begged. "I have heard many things about Him since my stay in Nidaros. But I would be very interested in hearing what you

have to say about Him and His new religion."

For the remainder of the ride King Olaf told his companion about Christianity. As they entered the town, the King ended his talk by saying, "Leif, I want you and your men to be baptized and become Christians. Exchange your Thor's hammer for a cross."

The following week Leif and Kettle discussed the new religion with the priests. They decided to accept Christianity. So did the six young men who had come with them. In due time, they and all their thralls were baptized in the fine wooden church Olaf had built in Nidaros.

One spring day Leif was summoned to the feasting hall by Olaf. The King was watching a clown juggle five wooden balls when Leif approached the high seat.

"Here, Leif," King Olaf called when he saw the Greenlander. "Sit here beside me. I have something important I want to discuss with you." He waved the juggler away and drew Leif down beside him.

"Leif," he began, "it's spring and sailing time again. And I know you'll want to be heading for Greenland."

Leif nodded. "With your permission, Sire."

"You have told me much about Greenland during your stay," the King went on seriously. "I understand your difficulty with traders. And I am ready to see that traders go to Greenland with iron and wood. But, Leif—" He paused and looked into the blue eyes of the young man beside him. "I have made laws that Norway will not trade with its colonies as long as the colonists believe in the old pagan gods. Get Christianity accepted as the religion of Greenland, Leif, and I shall see that you have trade."

"But, Sire," Leif protested. "I am not prepared to tell the people of my homeland about Christianity. I myself have been a follower of the White Christ just a short time."

"Well, then, I will send priests and teachers home with you," Olaf answered.

Leif thought of Eric and knew that his father would be angry when he saw the Christian teachers. Greenland could not exist much longer without trade. Leif made his decision. He would act for the good of the people, even though he hurt his father.

"Very well," Leif answered finally. "We'll take Christianity back to Greenland. Will your teachers be ready in a week? The dragon ship is already out of its winter shed and my thralls are preparing it to sail again."

"They'll be ready," promised the King. He stood up. "Leif, you and your men have been a great joy to me this winter season. You will henceforth always be welcome here. Go with my blessing and may fortune be with you."

A week later the ship was ready to sail. The hold was now full of lumber and wheat, for which Leif had traded his walrus ivory and hides. There was a fair wind blowing and the sail was raised. The oarsmen sat on the benches with their oars in place.

On the deck at the prow stood two brown-robed priests. Leif frowned every time he looked at them. What would Eric say when he saw them?

"It will be good to be out on the open sea in a dragon again," said Kettle as Leif steered the ship down the fiord away from Nidaros.

"Yes," Leif agreed. He stared up at the gulls circling over the ship. The red and white sail was vivid against the blue sky. "But it will not be good to face Eric's anger when he knows I have brought these priests of the White Christ to Greenland."

CHAPTER THIRTEEN

Leif Sails West

L EIF!" cried Thorhild as she hurried from
the stone church behind Eric's farm. "Wait!"

Leif turned in the path and watched his
mother hurry over the grassy slope toward
him. He pushed his iron helmet with the raven
wings on each side back from his forehead, as
the day was hot. Should he take a cow on the
journey, he wondered? Would there be
enough water? Suppose there were no springs
of fresh water in Bjarni's western lands?

Thorhild stepped into the path and caught
her son by the arm.

"I will walk with you to the boat landing,"
she said, falling into step with him. She
turned her head and smiled up at her tall,
handsome son. "I hope you will remember to

[*140*]

pray every day while you are on your voyage to the western lands, Leif."

Leif glanced down into his mother's face. "I will, Mother," he promised.

The bright summer sun glinted from his metal shield into his mother's eyes. He shifted it in his hand, remembering how quickly his mother had taken up Christianity. On his return from Norway two years before, Thorhild had welcomed the new religion at once. She had been baptized and had immediately put all Eric's thralls and those of her neighbors to work gathering stones for the fine chapel behind them. Now Thorhild spent many hours every day on her knees before the altar.

"And I hope you will try to persuade Eric to become a Christian," Thorhild went on. Lines of worry appeared in her face. Eric had been a trial to her during these past two years.

Leif had been right when he had predicted that Eric would be angry at the arrival of the priests. Greenland's old chief would have nothing to do with the new religion. Leif and Thorhild had both argued with him and attempted to show him what a strong new way of life was opened by the coming of the White Christ.

But Eric would not listen. He was rude to the monks. He sacrificed often in hope that Thor would destroy them. He continued to observe the feasts of the old gods.

Eric had been hurt and angry that his own son should have brought the priests to Greenland. He had almost ceased speaking to Leif since his return.

Leif, however, had gone quietly about the business of farming. He hoped, too, to make the western voyage he had planned so long. Perhaps when he had successfully explored these new lands, Eric would be proud of him and forgive him.

But the western sailing had been delayed for two more years. On Leif's return from Norway, he had gone to Bjarni Herjulfson to buy his ship. Bjarni wanted to make one last trip to Norway himself. "You shall have the ship as soon as I return," he promised Leif.

All the time Bjarni was gone, Leif fretted and worried. Suppose the ship were wrecked? Suppose Bjarni should lose the ship in a fight with some Berserker?

But Bjarni had come home this spring and turned the ship over to Leif. It had taken but a few weeks to make preparations. And this day, in the year 1002, Leif was ready to sail.

"Leif," Thorhild said, "you will try to persuade your father to become a Christian, won't you? This is so important to me. And I believe Eric will listen to you now. He was pleased that you asked him to lead the expedition."

Leif nodded. "Yes, I think he has almost forgotten he was so angry with me." He put his arm around his mother's shoulders. "I know how important it is to you," he told her. "And I will talk to Eric often while we are on board the ship. Maybe I can persuade him to give up the ways of Thor and Odin."

"Perhaps Eric will listen to you," Thorhild said. "He thinks a great deal of you, even though he doesn't show it. He admires the way you have run the farm. And he is proud of the way you sailed to and from Norway. Everyone is talking of the new route you took."

They reached the beach. A group of people stood on the shore. These were relations and friends of the forty Greenlanders who were making the voyage. They had come to bid Leif and his crew good-by.

The ship was ready. It lay at anchor in the quiet waters of the fiord. The sail flapped loosely from the mast. The oars were in place.

The after-boat, tied to the stern by a stout rope, rocked on the waves behind the ship.

"She looks sturdy, Leif," someone called.

Leif glanced at the ship proudly. It was not so graceful as a dragon, but it was strong and well built and much better suited for long voyages. Now it rode low in the water, for it was loaded with a winter's food supply.

"Come aboard, Leif," cried Kettle the Black, who was standing by the tiller.

Leif shook his head. "I'll wait for Father," he called.

"Eric is putting on all his best clothes," Thorhild explained. "I expect he mislaid his gold spurs. Tyrker will have him ready shortly."

Leif nodded. But he wished Eric would hurry.

Now his heart beat fast with excitement. By the time the summer's sun was overhead he and his ship would be on the open sea. A flock of little auks flew over and off toward the distant white mountains. Their shrill, noisy chattering came plainly over the water.

Leif glanced restlessly toward the house. He thought he saw a movement at the barn. Shading his eyes with his hand, he squinted in that

direction. It was Eric on his favorite horse.
Tyrker was walking behind.

"Yonder comes Father now," Leif exclaimed.

Thorhild turned and watched her husband's approach. Suddenly they saw the horse stumble. Eric jerked at the reins. The horse struggled to get its balance. But the ground was rough and the animal fell. Eric struck the ground and rolled away from the horse.

With a cry Leif sped up the path toward his father. When he reached Eric, Tyrker was helping him to his feet. "Are you hurt, Father?" asked Leif.

Eric tried to walk. He grimaced painfully and shook his head. "It's only a twisted ankle," he said shortly. "Is the horse all right?"

Leif glanced at the horse, now quietly grazing near by. "Yes," he answered. "Do you want to ride him the rest of the way down?"

Eric put his hand on Leif's shoulder. "No, I'll go back to the hall," he said slowly. "The fall was a sign, Leif. I have discovered Greenland, and one land is all the gods mean for me to discover. The expedition is yours and you must be the leader."

"But, Father—" protested Leif.

*The ground was rough and
the animal fell*

Eric shook his head. "We will say no more. I'm too old to go. I should be home by the hall fires, not out sea-roving. I'll say farewell now, and give you my luck and my blessing."

He kissed Leif on both cheeks and then took his hand. "Whoever your gods are, Leif, may they guide you in good fortune." Then he turned to the German. "Tyrker, you go with him. He needs one old head with him."

Back at the boat landing, Leif explained that his father had decided not to go. Farewells were said and best wishes given. The anchor was raised and the ship moved off down the fiord.

Eric waved to his mother and brothers. He saw his mother turn away and knew she was going to join Eric. He glanced up toward the farm. Not a figure was in sight. The farm looked peaceful and quiet with the green fields around. High over the farm one solitary great snowy owl hunted. It swooped low over the meadows and pounced. A moment later it soared upward with something in its talons, giving a thin cry.

Leif turned his eyes away from the land out toward the ocean ahead of them. He roared out an order to the oarsmen and turned the rudder slightly to bring the boat closer to shore.

In his heart Leif couldn't help being glad that Eric had not come. This was his boat, his crew, his voyage. His rightful place was in the steersman's seat. The ship sailed out of the fiord into the open sea.

West at last!

CHAPTER FOURTEEN

A New Land

FOR four days Leif sailed his ship toward
the setting sun. Kettle came to stand by Leif's
side on the fifth morning. "Leif," he asked,
"do you think we will make a landfall soon?"

"Yes," answered Leif. "I had good sailing
directions from Bjarni. And I do not doubt
but that by tomorrow we will sight land. I am
not worried about that. There is what worries
me." He pointed to three of the oarsmen who
stood talking together in the hold. One of
them was a thin, sour-looking man. "The crew
are restless and discouraged," Leif went on,
"and Rolf the Lean is stirring up trouble. I
should have left him in Greenland."

"Gold never satisfies a man like that," Kettle remarked. "Trouble is his pay."

Leif nodded. "I must remember to keep

him busy," he said. "Then he won't have time to encourage the others in their fears and doubts."

"Wasn't he one of Bjarni's crew?" asked Kettle.

"Yes," replied Leif. "Otherwise I wouldn't have hired him. I could tell he was a trouble-maker, but I wanted someone who had been with Bjarni on the voyage when he sighted the western lands."

"Never mind," soothed Kettle. "As soon as we find the land that Bjarni found, the others will forget Rolf's talk. We can put him to work now looking for land from the mast top."

"All right, Kettle, send him up," Leif said. Once more he scanned the horizon. How long before they would sight land, Leif wondered. Bjarni had said four days' sail with a fair wind. But there had been little wind to help Leif's ship.

Rolf reached the top of the mast. He clung there perilously for a few minutes, staring out over the ocean. Suddenly he gave a hoarse cry.

"Land! Land ahead!"

Rolf climbed down the ropes and ran to Leif.

"There's an icy mountain ahead," he cried.

"What did he see?" shouted one of the oarsmen at the front of the boat.

"A mountain ahead," roared Leif in answer.
"Take your places, all of you, and row like
true Viking men."

About the middle of the day the boat
reached the coast. The oarsmen stared in dis-
gust. Was this the new land they had come so
far to see? The flat shore land was nothing but
rock, bare and desolate. Not a tree nor a blade
of grass grew anywhere. A jumble of huge
boulders and rocky cliffs rose from the coast.
Behind this the glaciated mountain stood tall
and gloomy under gray clouds.

"Drop anchor and we'll go ashore in the
after-boat," shouted Leif.

"What!" cried Becan. "Do you mean to go
ashore on this dreary place?"

Leif grinned. "I won't be called a fool, as
Bjarni was, for not going ashore. I mean to put
my foot on every piece of land we find."

He chose ten men to go with him. When
they stepped on land, Leif could not repress a
shiver as he looked around. Lichen made hideous designs on the rock, but no other living
thing was in sight.

"Not even the cheerless land of the Frost

Giants is as mournful as this place," said Tyrker. "Look at that rock over there. It might very well be a giant's head."

Leif strolled toward the rock. His leather shoes slapped loudly on the bare stone. There was certainly nothing here to make a man leave his home and risk his life at sea. He doubted if there was even water here. Suddenly he stooped and picked up a black-and-white tern feather.

"Someone has been here before us," Leif laughed, holding up the feather. "But he didn't stay either. Let us return to the ship."

He led his companions among the rocks back to the ship's boat. As they rowed toward the ship, Leif said, "We will call this place Helluland, which means Land of Flat Stones."

They reached the ship and climbed aboard. It was late afternoon and Leif decided they should stay at anchor for the night. In the morning he steered toward the south. After several days Leif again noticed that Rolf was grumbling and trying to stir up trouble among the other oarsmen.

He called Kettle to take his place in the steersman's seat.

"I will have this out with Rolf right now," he told his friend. "This troublemaker has done enough damage."

Leif strode through the hold. Rolf was sitting on the block of wood in which the mast was held upright. Leif grabbed the troublemaker by his shirt and jerked him to his feet.

"Dog!" he thundered. "What flea is biting you now?" He shook him roughly.

Rolf cowered inside his woolen shirt. But he spoke up at last in a trembling voice.

"The fishes, not fleas, will soon be biting us," he said. "We'll be lost and never see Greenland again. You're headed wrong, Leif Ericson. Bjarni never sailed this route."

Leif turned Rolf loose so suddenly that the man fell back against the mast. "Rascal! Scoundrel!" roared Leif. "Would you like to take the after-boat and follow Bjarni's route alone?" He turned toward his crew. "Who among the rest of you is afraid to sail with Leif Ericson?" he asked. "Will you sail where I tell you to, or shall I carve a bloody eagle on your ribs?"

"We're with you, Leif," shouted Becan. Others took up the cry.

[*153*]

Dog!" he thundered. "What flea is
biting you now?"

A NEW LAND

Leif turned toward Rolf and asked, "Was not that land which I called Helluland Bjarni's last landfall?"

Rolf nodded. "There's no doubt about it," he affirmed. "A land such as that is not easily forgotten."

"We have found that landmark then," said Leif to the crew. "Bjarni told us there is plenty of land to the south. We did not come here to follow Bjarni's route, but to explore and discover for ourselves. There is no honor in going where another man has been. If you follow me to a new land, great fame may be yours."

There was a murmur of approval as Leif turned back toward the steering seat.

In a few days they did indeed sight a new land. This was very different from Helluland. The land was level and heavily wooded with large and beautiful evergreens. The beach, too, was flat and gently sloping, and everywhere they looked shining white sand stretched.

"What a beautiful place!" exclaimed Kettle.

"Let's go ashore, Leif," cried Becan. The others echoed the cry.

Leif and the others got in the after-boat and

rowed to shore, leaving only a few on board. They beached the boat and Leif led the way across the wide sandy shore. A moment later they were in the cool green shade of the forest.

"This land I shall name too, for its outstanding qualities," Leif told his men. "I shall call it Markland, or Forest Land."

They went deeper into the forests, for never

had they seen such trees. A wind sprang up from the northeast.

"Listen," said Tyrker.

The wind boiled and sang through the

needles of the larches and hemlocks. For a moment everyone stood still, listening to the song of the wind.

"It is blowing from the land," Leif said.

"And our ship will be blown out to sea without us. We had better hurry back."

They turned to go. But those in the front drew back in amazement. All around them sat a circle of great gray wolves. The men huddled together, while the wolves silently watched them.

"Wolves!" cried Tyrker. "Odin's animals! They have come to kill us all because you have deserted the god, Odin, and followed the White Christ!"

"Nonsense!" answered Leif. He strode forward. The wolves, which had never seen a man before, fell back cringing. Leif raised his battle-axe with a cry. The wolves scampered quickly away among the tree trunks.

"Come on, men," shouted Leif. "The wind is increasing. We must hurry."

The men followed Leif back to the after-boat. The wind was whipping the waves to a froth. The ship was tugging strongly at its anchor. Once on board the ship, Leif prepared for a storm. For two days the wind howled and the waves raged, as the ship drifted at the mercy of the wind.

Once again Rolf began to complain. "I

think we should turn back," he muttered to another of the oarsmen.

"No," the rower answered. "I have seen Leif Ericson walk through a circle of hungry wolves. Where Leif goes I am willing to follow, for luck will be with him and me."

CHAPTER FIFTEEN

Exploring Vinland

WHEN the storm stopped, the Greenlanders found themselves on the open ocean.

"Shall you sail back to Markland now?" Kettle asked Leif.

Leif shook his head. "No," he answered. "I believe there is more land to the south. I will sail on."

Kettle laughed. "Good!" he exclaimed. "I for one am eager to see all I can of this new world. And I believe the men will follow you to the ends of the earth."

Leif smiled at his friend as his hand tightened on the tiller. But as he gazed at the empty horizon he wondered if he was right in sailing farther south. Perhaps he should go back to Markland and take home a cargo of the timber which Greenland so badly needed. But somehow he felt that better things lay ahead of him.

Perhaps, if he dared to sail on, he would find a land rich in many things besides timber. Such a land would make Greenland less dependent on trade with merchant ships from Norway. These ships did not come often since the death of King Olaf.

Leif knew that Eric would be very much pleased with such a discovery. He might even forgive his son for having brought Christianity to Greenland. Besides, Markland might have been enough for some men to discover, but not for Leif Ericson. The old lure of the west and strange lands led him on.

On the morning of the second day, a rocky headland loomed over the sea's edge. It didn't look very promising. But Leif sailed along the coast, looking for a harbor. At last the ship rounded a point of land and came into a shallow bay.

The tide was going out so rapidly that the ship was left stranded. So the men jumped overboard and splashed ashore. Only Leif was left on the tilted ship. He stood at the prow, staring at the new land. Was this what he had been looking for all these years? Was this the place he had been meant to come? What was waiting here for him—riches and honor and fame? Or perhaps danger and even death?

Suddenly Leif smiled and leaped lightly overboard. Whatever lay ahead of him, he had come seeking it. He would go to meet it with zest and courage, he told himself, as he waded toward the shore.

The men explored the beach. They found a river leading to a small lake. When the tide came in and the ship floated once again, they towed the ship up the river and moored it.

Leif ordered the men to bring their sleeping bags ashore. "We will stay here awhile and hunt and explore," Leif told them.

But Rolf the Lean refused to sleep on shore. He said he was afraid this country was inhabited and that the people might attack him in the night. So he intended to sleep on the ship.

Leif turned away. He did not answer Rolf, because in his heart he, too, feared the land might be inhabited. But he said nothing, because he did not wish to alarm the crew.

In the morning, leaving five men to guard the ship, the rest set out to explore the woods. They walked along the shore of the lake. The September sun was shining hot and bright. In the clear water the men could see large salmon

and other fishes. Across the lake a flock of water fowl made loud honking noises.

They turned away and crossed a meadow of
waist-high grass. At their approach two deer
bounded away into the forest.

"This is indeed a land of plenty," remarked
Tyrker. "Already we have found fish and fowl
and meat enough to feed the army of the King
of Norway."

"Yes," Leif added, looking pleased, "and
look at this grass. All the cows in Greenland
could feed here."

They came to the edge of the woods. For a
moment Leif stood gazing in among the trees.
How cool and green and dim it seemed in the
forest compared to the bright sunlight here.
And surely no human being had ever set foot
here before. He could see no trails or paths or
any signs that timber had been cut.

Leif walked under the trees. A scarlet bird
with black wings and tail flew ahead of him.
"Look at that bird!" exclaimed Leif.

"What kind of a tree is this?" asked Tyrker.
"Its bark is as shaggy as Becan's head."

Becan grinned. "It's better to be shaggy-
headed than bow-legged as you are, you old
troll!"

They came to the edge of the woods

Leif looked around. "None of these trees are like the ones we know," he said.

"They're giant trees," Kettle exclaimed. "Look at the size of that one over there!"

He pointed to a tree with smooth silver-gray bark. Its trunk was enormous and free of knots. All around him, Leif noticed other big trees, which seemed to rise up to the clouds. Never had he dreamed there were such huge trees, or trees of so many different kinds. Here was timber enough to build a whole fleet of dragons and trading ships for Greenland. Wait until Eric heard of this!

Four men joined hands and tried to circle one of the big trunks. Still the hands of the first and fourth man did not quite meet.

"It is like the ash tree, Yggdrasill, that supported heaven and earth," said Tyrker in an awed tone.

They went forward again slowly. Leif took note of the direction so that they might not become lost. Suddenly, overhead, there was the sound of hammering. Leif looked up. A large black bird with a tall red crest and an enormous bill was whacking at a dead branch. As Leif watched, the bird flew away with a loud call.

"It sounds as if it were laughing at us," Becan said.

They moved forward among the big tree trunks. The light was very dim, almost like twilight under the layers of thick foliage overhead. How quiet it was! The men's voices sounded strange and overloud.

"What a lonely place this is," thought Leif.

One of the men gave a shout and ran toward him with something in his hand. "See what I have found among the roots of that tree," he exclaimed.

It was a stick of wood shaped, Leif thought, like a kind of club. The wood was light in color and at the end of the club was a round knob. On the knob a face had been carved—a strange human face with narrow eyes and high cheekbones. A row of tiny men was burned into the wood along the length of the club.

Leif hefted it in his hand and swung it through the air. "It is a war club, I'm sure," he said at last.

Rolf spoke up quickly, "I was right. This land *is* inhabited."

Several of the men began to murmur in disappointment. Leif knew how they felt. He, too, had hoped that he and his men would not have to share this land with anyone else. His group was too small to put up much of a fight. And if the inhabitants proved unfriendly, they would have to sail back to Greenland empty-handed. But Leif was determined that the men should not know his fears.

"This club looks very old," he said. "It was probably left here many years ago by some visitor like ourselves. When my father first reached Greenland, he found skin boats and stone weapons there. But you yourselves know that we never saw any people there except ourselves."

He stopped and looked around at the men's faces. Would they lose heart and want to go home, having come so far?

"Listen!" whispered Rolf the Lean.

They stood in the dim light with the gnarled old trunks around them. There was not a sound. In the green light, shadows seemed to move menacingly. Leif seemed to feel eyes staring at him from among the leaves. He was sure there was no one there. Yet he was afraid and he knew the men were afraid. These trees were so old and so big. It was so dim and lonely and silent under their branches.

A leaf drifted slowly down and brushed his

face. Leif gave a start. Far off, the black wood-pecker gave its queer laugh. Then the silence came back, deeper than ever.

"Let us go back to the ship," said Tyrker in a harsh voice.

The men wheeled as one man and began to run back the way they had come. Only Leif, Kettle, and Becan were left standing together.

"Stop!" thundered Leif. "Are you cowards that you run from nothing? Stay where you are, and the first man that moves will get my sword in his vitals!"

The men stopped and turned back reluc-tantly. Huddled together, they waited while Leif made a rude cross of wood to mark the spot where they had stood. Then he picked up the war club and turned to the crew.

"Kettle," he said. "Lead the way to the ship. And since my oarsmen are so faint-hearted that they run from shadows, I will bring up the rear to see that no shadows run after us."

The men looked sheepish, but as they walked back through the woods they spoke in low tones. They glanced sidewise at the gloomy forest on either hand and walked close to each other.

As he followed his men, Leif was heavy-hearted. Though most of the men were Christians, he knew that many of them still believed in witches and magic. He knew that such men might become panic-stricken if they found themselves alone in the forest. They might lose their heads and run deeper and deeper into the woods. Perhaps they might never be found again. He would have to take precautions to make sure none of them was ever alone in the woods.

They reached the camp at last. That day Leif divided the men into two groups.

"Kettle will lead one group," he told the men. "And I will lead the other. One day Kettle will hunt and explore, while we stay and guard the camp. The next day it will be our turn to hunt, and Kettle's group will be guards."

The days passed. Still there were no signs of any other people. The hunting was excellent. The men soon grew familiar with the surrounding forest. The strangeness they had felt at first in the woods was gone.

Now, too, fall had really come.

"This is surely the most beautiful country in the world," exclaimed the Norsemen at the sight of the autumn colors. Scarlet and crimson, orange and yellow blazed in the woods on every side.

Great flocks of duck and geese flew over on their way south. Many stopped in the lake where the ship was moored. Leif's men feasted on them.

Leif was sure now that the war club had been dropped by a chance visitor, and not by an inhabitant.

"We will stay the winter here," he told the Vikings. "There is food in plenty and no one to bother us. We will build snug houses for cold weather."

The men were glad to stay. They fell to work building the houses at once.

One day Leif was busy directing his group in building a cabin. He looked up and saw Kettle's men coming hurriedly from the woods. As they advanced, they looked back over their shoulders as though in fear.

Leif went to meet them. "Where is Kettle?" he demanded.

"He and two others are still in the woods," answered one of the men.

"In the woods!" repeated Leif angrily. "Have I not given orders that you were not to separate in the forest?"

"He stayed to search for Tyrker," another spoke up. "But we were afraid."

"Is Tyrker lost?" cried Leif. "Why did you let him out of your sight? He's an old man and you should have looked after him."

"We'll have nothing to do with a witch!" shouted Rolf the Lean. "The old German is a shape-changer. He stepped into some bushes and when we went to look for him he was gone. In his place was a hideous animal with hands on its head."

"Kettle stayed to look for the evil one," another remarked. "But we knew Tyrker was up to witchcraft. I have seen shape-changers before and I know."

Leif was beside himself with fury. "You call yourselves Christians!" he roared. "You know there is no such thing as witchcraft or shape-changing. No, you have come running home and left an old man to die in the jaws of some strange beast. What cowards you are! Quickly —show me where you left Kettle."

The men grumbled and protested, but they led Leif back to the spot where Kettle and Tyrker had disappeared.

"Tyrker went right into those bushes," said Rolf in a whisper.

Suddenly from the underbrush there came a sound of crackling twigs. Then there was a most terrible bellow.

"That's him!" cried Rolf. The men fled with shouts of fear.

The crackling came nearer. Leif stood his ground, gripping his battle-axe tighter. There was a sound of snorting and stamping of huge hoofs. Through the bushes appeared the strangest creature Leif had ever beheld. For a minute he almost thought that only magic could have produced this big deer with its beard and drooping nose and antlers like two upturned hands.

But Leif had seen many curious sights in this new land. He refused to believe that every new kind of beast was a witch in the form of an animal.

Now the animal saw Leif. With a loud bellow it lowered its head and prepared to charge. As the moose thundered toward him, Leif crossed himself. The antlers were almost touching him. He could see the bloodshot eyes and wet nostrils. Swiftly he jumped aside and brought the axe down on the beast's skull.

With another tremendous bellow the moose staggered and fell dead. Leif looked down at

*He brought the axe down on the
beast's skull*

the fallen animal. It was the largest and strangest deer he had ever seen.

At the sound of running feet, he looked up to find Kettle running toward him. "Leif!" he gasped. "What happened? Are you hurt?"

Leif did not bother to answer. "Where's Tyrker?" he asked.

"I wish I knew," Kettle answered. "He disappeared right before our eyes. Now I can't find him anywhere."

"There he comes now," cried a man behind Leif. He and the others had returned when they saw that Leif had killed the so-called witch.

"Tyrker!" cried Leif happily. "Where have you been?"

The old German looked very small and shrunken under the big trees. But he stepped along lightly. His face was wreathed in smiles.

"Where have you been?" cried Leif again.

Tyrker held up something in his hand and spoke several words Leif could not understand.

"He's speaking German," explained Kettle. "What's the matter with him?"

"Foster Father!" shouted Leif. "What are you saying?"

Tyrker looked up. Though he was still smiling, his eyes were full of tears.

"Grapes, Leif!" he exclaimed. "I found grapes!"

"Grapes!" the men shouted together. They crowded around the old man to see the fruit he held in his hand.

"Are you sure, Foster Father?" asked Leif. "For I have never seen grapes and don't know what they look like."

"Oh, yes," Tyrker answered. "In the forest of my old home in Germany there were many grapevines. When I tasted the grape, I thought I was a boy at home again. And that was the reason I spoke in German."

"Now we know how really blessed our voyage has been," said Leif. "For this is the best discovery of all." He looked around at the men. "Now we have two jobs before us. Each day we shall gather grapes or cut vines and fell trees. This will be the cargo I will take home to Greenland."

With this work the winter passed quickly. The grapes were gathered and either dried or made into wine. Timber for boats and houses was cut and stored on the ship. Grapevines were stored on board too. These would be used to replace hard-to-get rope. The winter weather was mild, compared to Greenland, and the men were able to work outdoors all during the cold months.

In the spring they made ready to depart. The ship with its cargo was towed down to the sea. The Vikings took their places at the oars once more.

As Leif steered the ship away from the land, he turned to give one last look. "I think I will call this land Vinland," he said to Kettle, "because it gave us such rich gifts of vines and grapes."

He gazed once more at the great forest. "From the time I was a child," he went on, "I have dreamed of sailing to the west and exploring a new country. But never in my wildest dreams did I expect to find a country so wonderful, so beautiful, and so rich. I have left my houses here, with my name carved over the doors. May God grant that soon I shall set foot again on this marvelous shore!"

CHAPTER SIXTEEN

Leif the Lucky

LEIF steered his ship safely to Greenland. When the mountains of his home were in sight, Leif's keen eyes spotted a wreck on a reef. None of the others could even see the reef, but Leif could see people and a ship-wrecked vessel. He steered his ship to the reef and rescued a rich trader named Thori, and his wife, and all his crew.

"This is a miracle," said Thori. "We had given up hope of being rescued. We were afraid no ship would ever see us. All my cargo is yours now, Leif, and it is a rich one."

Now at last Leif steered his ship up the fiord to his own home. All of Eric's household came running to greet him and to hear the news of his voyage. Eric was delighted with his discoveries. Thorvald and Thorstein were proud of their brother's new wealth and honor. And

[*177*]

Thorhild wept with happiness to see her son.

There was much feasting and entertainment that summer in honor of Leif. Over and over again the Greenlanders had to hear the story of Leif's voyage and praise him for his skill and daring.

"Thanks to Leif, Greenland will not want for anything!" Eric cried one day as they all sat in the feast hall.

"He should be called Leif the Lucky," spoke up Thorstein. "For has he not brought riches and honors to us all? Was he not the first to sail to Norway without stopping at Iceland?

Did not he save these fine people from certain death on the reef? And finest of all, did he not sail to the west where no man has been before and discover a land of plenty which will make Greenland the richest land in the world? Surely we will call him Lucky, for whatever he does prospers!"

Unfortunately, Eric died that winter. Leif took over his father's duties and the following spring he was not able to return to Vinland as he had hoped. Instead he lent his ship to Thorvald, who sailed away to the new country. Thorvald never returned and his men brought back bad news. They had found that Vinland was truly inhabited. In a battle with these strange copper-colored inhabitants, whom the Norsemen called skraelings, Thorvald had been killed by an arrow.

As the years passed, several other Norsemen made voyages to Vinland. But the greatest was that of a man named Thorfinn Karlsefni. In 1010 A.D., he took several ships and a large number of people to Vinland, as well as goods and cattle. He was determined to colonize the new land. They stayed three years, but the copper-colored skraelings warred against them continuously. Karlsefni realized that a colony would never be established there. He and his people returned to Greenland. The Greenlanders continued to make voyages to this new land, but they never tried to make homes there again.

Among the people of Iceland and Greenland the story of Leif's discoveries was told over and over again and written down in sagas. But the rest of the world, if they heard of Vinland at all, soon forgot about it.

When Columbus sailed to America in 1492, Europeans thought he was the first to arrive there. With the invention of guns and gunpowder, Europeans were able to defeat the Indians and settle the country. But even with these new inventions it was a long, hard fight. It is easy to see why a handful of Norsemen with swords and battle-axes could not fight the copper-colored skraelings in the New World.

Today the sagas which were written so long ago are widely known. The Greenland settlements in the New World have vanished from the earth, but today we honor Leif Ericson. Today we know that this Viking chieftain was the first white man of whom it is recorded that he set foot on the shores of the continent of North America.

Pronouncing Guide
to the Scandinavian Names

Becan (*beh*-kahn)
Berserker (ber-*serk*-er)
Bjarni (*byarn*-ee)
Bolli (*boh*-lee)
Bragi (*brah*-gee)
Egil (*eh*-gil)
Eric (*ehr*-ik)
Ericson (*ehr*-ik-sun)
Eyolf (*ay*-yohlf)
Faroë (fah-*roh*-uh) (in English, *fay*-roh)
Fiord (fyord)
Gunnar (*goo*-nahr)
Gunnbjorn (*goon*-byorn)
Helluland (*hel*-oo-lahnd)
Herjulfson (*hehr*-yoolf-sohn)
Hodur (*hoh*-dur)
Hrut (hroot)
Karlsefni (kahrl-*sef*-nee)
Leif (leef)
Nidaros (nih-*dar*-ohs)
Odin (*oh*-din)
Olafson (*oh*-lahf-sohn)

Orkney (*ork*-nee)
Rolf (rohlf)
Skerries (*skehr*-eez)
Skraeling (*skral*-ing)
Sleipnir (*slyp*-neer)
Snorrison (*snohr*-ih-sohn)
Styr (stihr)
Thing (ting)
Thor (tor) (in English, thor)
Thorfinn (*tor*-fin)
Thorgest (*tor*-gest)
Thorgils (*tor*-gils)
Thorhild (*tor*-hild)
Thori (*tor*-ee)
Thorstein (*tor*-styn)
Thorvald (*tor*-vahld)
Tryggvason (*trig*-vah-sohn)
Tyrker (*tihr*-ker)
Uggason (*oog*-gah-sohn)
Ulfsson (*oolf*-sohn)
Vinland (*vin*-lahnd)
Viking (*vy*-king)
Yggdrasill (*ig*-drah-sil)

About the Author

WILLIAM O. STEELE was born in Franklin, Tennessee, where, as a boy, he hunted the fresh-plowed fields for weapons of earlier times. He hoped to find some cast-aside spear of Madoc's band, or some Viking axe lost in a battle with the Indians. However, his hopes were ill-founded, he learned in college. But his interest in pre-Columbian contacts with America had begun and was to continue after his graduation from college in 1940 and through five years in the armed forces. Now, from his deep personal interest, comes his first story of the Vikings, a departure from his many pioneer books for boys and girls.

About the Artist

PRANAS LAPÉ was born in Lithuania where he went through high school and attended the Kaunas Art Institute. When World War II started, the institute was closed, and he spent the next two years hiding from the German occupation army. He tried to escape to Paris but was arrested and sent to a labor battalion in Finland to build airports. Later he did escape and reached Sweden. There he learned the war was over, so he went to work in a ceramics factory, taught art, and also illustrated books for Swedish publishers. Pranas Lapé waited four years for the chance to come to America, and finally arrived here in 1949.

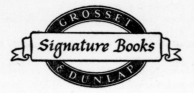

"Names That Made History"

ENID LAMONTE MEADOWCROFT, *Supervising Editor*

1 Born at Haukadal, Iceland, in 973

2 Bids outlawed father farewell from Ox Island, Iceland, 982

3 Hears of Greenland on father's return to Iceland, 985

4 Reaches Greenland with his family, 986

10 Dies in Greenland, 1020

9 Returns to Greenland and receives nickname of Leif the Lucky, 1003